A LITTLE
RED WAGON

full of hope

TIPS AND INSPIRATION
FROM A LOVING CAREGIVER

Kathy Scanlon Opie

DEDICATION

I dedicate this book to my father, Dr. John W. Scanlon, who passed away in November 2014. I received my love of writing from him, a love we shared and a gift he encouraged in me. In the same way, my dad encouraged us to fight to get a solid diagnosis of Conner's illness at a time when Paul and I didn't know what to do. He championed this book from its beginning, giving me courage to ask our wonderful surgeon, Dr. Chappie Conrad, to write the foreword for this book. An accomplished author himself and not one to hold back constructive criticism, my father beamed with pride when he called to tell me that this heartfelt book would help many people. I'm truly grateful that my dad was able to read the finished manuscript before he left us. All the love, support, and inspiration he gave us are woven through the pages of this book. Yes, Dad, this book will serve as a wonderful outreach, and may your kindness and memory live on each time it's read.

Copyright© 2015 Kathy Scanlon Opie
All rights reserved.
Library of Congress ISBN-13:978-1-93899-08-3
ISBN: 10-1938990080
Library of Congress Control Number: 2015934387

Published by: Gabriel's Horn, Minneapolis, MN USA

G/H

Developmental edit and project management: Marlene Blessing
Book design: Constance Bollen, cbgraphics
Cover design: Bong Bernardino

Front cover photo: Little girl walking down the path pulling red wagon
with teddy bear © Nuli | Dreamstime.com
Back cover photo: Copyright© Paul "Mooselips" Dudley

CONTENTS

Foreword

Cancer affects almost every family in America. When it affects a parent, it's a major life challenge. When it affects a child, it's a bigger challenge. Add a "rare" tumor diagnosis in an unusual location, and you have one of the biggest challenges a family can face. The story of Conner Opie's treatment for Ewing's sarcoma and his family's struggles through that treatment is a story of loving parents, a good family and caring friends trying to be supportive on a daily basis during twelve months of chemotherapy, hospital admissions, clinic visits, and multiple surgical procedures. It is a time when a family and their child and friends are required to put their personal and professional lives on hold and spend the vast majority of their time in a hospital, trusting a medical team that has suddenly become a major part of their lives.

Accepting this diagnosis and its treatment is extremely challenging: all of this change and challenge happens on a dime. Navigating this change and maintaining some emotional balance requires major support from your family, friends, care providers and, if you are lucky, a "sarcoma support group," a group of sarcoma supporters who know the details of what treatment involves and what the patient and family challenges will be before, during, and after they happen. Such support groups for this and other diseases may arise spontaneously or represent online, offline, local, regional, or national organizations, but are most valuable when they are local and immediately available. The most important support resource for you and your family, next to your friends and a caring and expert treatment team, is a sarcoma support group (or one related to the disease your loved one is fighting). The best sarcoma support groups are local and connected to you. They have run this race, know what is at the finish line and can understand the challenges.

Other support resources are important, and Kathy Opie's book A *Little Red Wagon Full of Hope* is an example of one of those resources for families dealing with a sarcoma or other life-threatening illness. Its valuable advice for caregivers includes such things as "How to Bring Home to the Hospital" to "Food for the Soul" or "Pet Therapy." Her book makes a contribution in a very practical and personal way because of the specifics of her suggestions, exemplified by her multiple lists of things to consider, things to bring to the hospital, even a listing of potential faux pas to avoid before they happen; all from a mom who just finished her experience.

Although most children survive their disease, "tolerating" the race to recover successfully includes finishing treatment with an intact family and child who can return to their normal, happy lives. That journey is usually more challenging for the parents than it is for the child. With such resources as a supportive family, a good treatment team, and support groups, your chances of surviving your disease and the emotional challenges of treatment are good. Adding Kathy Opie's A *Little Red Wagon Full of Hope* to your support team will only improve your odds!

"Chappie" Conrad, M.D.

PREFACE

I never imagined I would lose my best friend to cancer or that, eight years later, our youngest son would be diagnosed with Ewing's Sarcoma, a rare form of bone cancer. It was as if lightning had struck twice in the same place. Why did a young mother have to die? Why did our child have to suffer? I pondered these hard questions and stumbled through the haze of the first months of our son's cancer treatment. In the midst of my caregiver's journey, I began to realize that perhaps there was something I could learn from the experience. Whether our son survived or not, I knew I'd never be the same. There would be others who would face such crises, with similar fears, questions, and needs for comfort and compassion. If I could illuminate the way for someone else through my stories and offer a glimmer of hope from a dark time in our lives, I would have gained something from our journey.

I'm not a professional counselor, although I have a master's in school psychology and was an elementary and middle school counselor before I had my own children. I've given advice I feel may be helpful to a family or loved ones in a caregiving role. My suggestions come from personal knowledge and from interviewing others who have experienced similar situations. Writing this book has inspired me to become a licensed family and marriage counselor, building upon my previous psychology background. It's my hope to combine my experience with a formal education and become more effective in my outreach.

Through my volunteer work with the Northwest Sarcoma Foundation, I've gained a deeper understanding of the plights of others and of the power of connecting with the community of support that exists. The compassionate care given through NW Sarcoma's community outreach programs goes a long way in helping patients and their families cope with illness, as do similar programs offered by other health-related nonprofits. I've learned that care doesn't stop at diagnosis and treatment. It continues long after. To find a cure for sarcoma and other forms of cancer, there is a critical need for more research funding.

During our son's treatment, I relied heavily on my Christian faith to surmount many obstacles. I'm aware that others may have different belief systems and have great respect for that. I used my stories to illustrate that relying on something greater than ourselves gives us strength and hope when everything seems impossible and completely beyond our power.

Without the help of friends, family, and our community, there was absolutely no way our family could have survived. I had been a member of that community when my best friend was sick, that same community came to our aid when our son had cancer. In whatever circumstance you may find yourself—whether as a caregiver or a friend or family member of someone facing a life-threatening illness—your best response is to ask, "How can I help?"

Acknowledgments

I'd like to acknowledge several people who made this book possible. I'd like to thank my editor, Marlene Blessing, whose thoughtful and honest editing help to create a more cohesive story. My writing teacher Brenda Peterson had the vision to create a caregiver's book from a memoir, understanding that many people would benefit. The feedback and support of our writing class proved invaluable in shaping many chapters of this book. Constance ("CB") Bollen turned a manuscript into a beautiful book with her design talents. And photographer Paul ("Mooselips") Dudley donated a photo shoot for the image that appears on the back cover of this book.

I'd like to thank my husband, Paul, who encouraged me to write and edit despite the painful material covered. Thank you for believing in me and letting me spend hours writing without complaint.

I'd like to thank our daughter, Jennifer, who persevered 3,000 miles away from home her sophomore year of college while we were consumed with Conner's care. During school breaks, she selflessly offered her support. We're very proud of the young woman she's become.

Our son Patrick discovered the healing gift of music while his brother was in treatment. He also qualified for the Washington State 500m freestyle right after his brother's surgery. He could've celebrated with his team, but he chose to return to his brother at the hospital. We're proud of how close the kids have become through this experience.

Thank you Conner for your inspiration. You beat the monster cancer, and did so courageously and without wanting to attract attention to yourself. We learned much from your quiet example.

I want to thank my Dad, who told me to never give up and to champion our son's cause when we weren't getting the answers we needed. Do you know that 80 percent of children's cancers are metastasized upon diagnosis? I'd like to thank my family who rallied and came to our side during treatment with visits, cards, and calls to support us when we didn't think we had the strength to keep going.

To my friends Jeanne Miele, Monica Skibeness, Patti Evans, Tracy Ayers-Tate, Adrian Harden, Michelle Melillo, and Wendy Frazier who met to create Care Calendar for our family, and for the countless friends and neighbors who brought meals, walked our dogs, care-sat, and sent packages, notes, emails, and phone calls of support.

I'd like to thank the staff and volunteers at Seattle Children's Hospital; Chappie, our nurses, Sue and Kristin, and Conner's tutor, Kathy. A big thank-you to my Wing's Mammas, Diane Simpson, Karen Fantozzi, Paula Yost, Kayla Black, Barb Wilson, Anita Maling, and Diana Dickerson. I'd like to thank the men who interviewed for the male caregiver's chapter; Kiyo Dickerson, Tom Mahoney, Jeff Fantozzi, Michael Brown, Dan Simpson, and Albert Rillos. And finally, the NW Sarcoma Foundation for your ongoing support of families fighting this dreadful disease. A portion of the sales profit of this book will go back to support the foundation.

1

WHAT CAN I DO TO HELP?

Our teenage son Conner had been complaining of right arm pain for months. The trips to the doctors and area clinics provided no answers. After a harrowing night of explosive shoulder pain and another fruitless trip with him to the neighborhood clinic, I insisted on a visit to Seattle Children's Hospital. There he underwent a two-day series of MRIs, blood work, and exams conducted by the head of the orthopedics department. Instead of his doctor giving us the results of these extensive tests, the following scenario occurred as Conner and I opened the door to the examining room.

"Hello, Mrs. Opie." Dr. Song extended his hand in greeting, yet I was frozen, unable to shake his hand as I saw the spectacle before me. Dr. Song reached for the ribbon of standard-issue hospital identification stickers that dangled from my limp wrist, on which were printed Conner's name, birth date, and hospital I.D. number. Little did I know that these would become our hospital passports for the next ten months and beyond. I had just been given these minutes earlier by the receptionist in the check-in area.

"You already know me and I've invited a few of my colleagues to join us." I heard a string of titles: Director of Pediatric Oncology, Director of Pediatric Orthopedic Oncology Surgery, Oncology Fellow, Oncology Resident, Pediatric Fellow, Pediatric Orthopedic Surgical Resident. My head began to whirl out of control. I was greeted with pained smiles and hands were offered for me to shake.

The team of doctors was here to deliver the devastating news that my son had a potential diagnosis of a rare form of bone cancer in his right scapula. It was October 2008, and Conner was just thirteen years old. The biopsy scheduled in one week would confirm the diagnosis. That day, my world began to crumble.

Eventually, I would learn to piece it back together. As the mother of a cancer survivor, I wanted to write this book to share my experience with caregivers and the community of friends and family who support loved ones faced with similar life-threatening situations. I hope the many things I learned in caring for my son will offer helpful ideas, insights, and, most of all, inspiration for this challenging journey.

Diagnosis

The week after our first visit to the hospital, Conner and I entered the examining room and found six white coat–clad men standing before us. As the tallest doctor in the room began to speak, I started to feel the floor give way beneath me like quicksand. I realized that I could no longer hear what was being said to me. I just remember telling myself, *Whatever you do, don't cry in front of Conner!*

"Mrs. Opie?" I heard the doctor pause to gain my attention. "Do you have any questions for us?" I stood up straight, attempting to make myself as large as possible, so I could look each doctor square in the eye as I issued the following command. "Move as fast as you can," I said through gritted teeth, my fists clenched. It was either fight or flight. As the doctors slowly exited the room, I chose to fight.

"Mom, you aren't going to cry are you?" Conner stepped forward and draped an awkward teenage arm over my shoulder in support. Tears pricked and burned at the sides of my eyes. When I worked as a school counselor, I had helped many young students through crises. Why was I standing here helpless and frozen?

"They said it was only a 50/50 chance it was cancer, so don't freak out already." I heard my son's adolescent voice echo through the room trying to reassure me. He was still so innocent and had no idea of the extreme challenges that lay ahead. *This is my soccer-playing, animal shelter volunteer son whom I love with all my heart,* I said to myself, trembling within. I couldn't imagine losing him. I reached over and held him as I promised, "Conner, it's going to be okay. We're going to be okay," hoping to convince myself as much as Conner.

Almost immediately, a matronly nurse appeared in the doorway to offer assistance. I knew by her kindly smile and serious eyes that she had experience in these matters. I was grateful for her calm strength as she took my arm and led me to the hall phone, where I called my husband, Paul. He arrived within minutes, dressed in his business suit. The six lab coats returned to our exam room to re-explain the grim news. It was like a war briefing. The second time around was not easier. It just made the situation more real.

On October 29, 2008, we received Conner's official diagnosis of Stage 3 Ewing's Sarcoma, bone cancer. The tumor had originated in his glenoid joint (armpit) and was the size of an orange. We would need a bone donor to replace half of his scapula and cartilage to repair part of his shoulder joint. Conner would then undergo ten months of in-patient chemotherapy. Three months after that, depending on whether the tumor shrank sufficiently and was inactive enough to be safely operated upon without spreading to other parts of the body, Conner's tumor would be removed and his shoulder rebuilt. If too many cancer cells remained after the surgery, radiation therapy would be recommended.

Our news was wrenching. It was cancer. This affected not only Conner and our immediate family, but also our entire extended family and community of friends, neighbors, and other supporters. The helplessness we felt after Conner's diagnosis was confirmed and radiated outward. Everyone we knew wanted to do something to help. At first, many offered a sympathetic ear, a shoulder to cry on, or a hug. Then the questions started. When will you start treatment? What is the prognosis? What will you need? We didn't have all the answers; but we did know we couldn't do this alone.

Our surgeon told us their hope was that Conner would regain 75 percent usage of his right arm. Paul and I were thankful for Conner's limb-salvaging surgery. To say we were completely overwhelmed would have been an understatement. Appointments were made, and we were given a huge three-ring binder entitled "Caring for Your Child with Cancer." It was full of information we needed to learn about our son's disease in order to administer care to him.

We received extensive lists describing what we could and couldn't do with our son. Feelings of helplessness, anger, confusion, and fear threatened to overcome us on a daily basis. It was difficult to keep our feelings in check around our three children, assuring them everything would be okay when sometimes we barely felt that way ourselves. Learning how to cope with these new emotions, ask for help, and take Conner's new situation one day (or sometimes even one hour) at a time were important skills we had to develop. The information overload was one thing; but grieving the loss not only of Conner's former life but our own was an entirely new experience. Our friends and community wanted to help in any way they could. We digested the news of Conner's health each day as well as we could, some days better than others. We knew many just like us were trying their best to cope as well.

Asking Friends and Family for Support

It was not easy for me to ask for or accept help at first. I had always been the friend or the neighbor who helped everyone else. One of our friends actually thanked me for letting people support us. Over time, I realized that in accepting help, I was giving people a chance to convert their own feelings of powerlessness into aid that eased their struggle and our pain. I learned to free myself of expectations about who should help us. More than once, I was disappointed by someone I anticipated would step forward to help who didn't, while surprised, gladdened, and humbled by others who came forward unexpectedly.

I had so much information to share with the many well-meaning people who called and stopped by with questions. I remember one of my closest friends asking me to start a CaringBridge website to blog regular updates on our activities, treatment, and prognosis. I was so unversed in social media at the time that I didn't even have a Facebook account. Initially, I balked at the idea. But knowing how much I loved to journal, my family and friends gently coaxed me into starting it. They understood better than I what a catharsis this activity would provide for me. It was so easy to set up my blog. This wonderful website graciously handled the burden of responding to my multiple phone calls and countless emails. Through the free CaringBridge social media, hundreds could keep in touch with our family and stay connected, sending and receiving messages throughout the week.

My friends and family would often call and stop by to ask us what we needed. I remember one of my friends being particularly concerned about what we were going to do with our dogs while we were at the hospital and what sorts of household chores needed to be done during the week. She also seemed quite interested in our food preferences. When I began to get suspicious, she feigned another call coming in and quickly ended the call with me. The following week, Jeanne surprised me by asking me to turn on my computer and click onto the CareCalendar.org website. I opened the web browser and the image of a sweet little hand holding a daisy popped onto my screen. Jeanne then gave me a password to type into the field and told me that our friends had created an account for our family.

"We all got together and organized a work party, made a list of chores, meals, and other tasks for us to take care of while you guys are at the hospital during chemotherapy treatment," Jeanne beamed. My eyes began to water and my throat tightened. I was overcome with emotion and a sense of love. The goodwill from my friends and community began to flood over me, and I hugged her tightly.

"Look, look here. You see this calendar? There are slots where we have listed chores like dog walking on the days you are at the hospital, and meals for the days you are home and care sitting for Conner, and the days you need to run to the store or take a break and you need someone to watch Conner," Jeanne pointed out, a bit embarrassed by my sudden display of emotion.

I looked at the online calendar, which resembled a large kitchen wall calendar, with a large square for the day of the week and slots for the hours of the day. When people signed up for a meal, for instance, they could list the foods they were bringing and the time they were delivering the meal.

"Paul gave me an email list of all your friends and neighbors, so I can send reminders and requests when there are needs to be filled. If you can think of more people, let me know. The CareCalendar website also sends out reminders," Jeanne explained. "And you can let me know as things come up or you need additional help. When new people volunteer, I can add them to the calendar, too." Jeanne waved her hand in front of her face to keep me from seeing her own tears and continued tutoring me on all the great features of the website.

This, along with the CaringBridge website, was a great resource. All the information on CareCalendar was well-organized and accessible so that I could review it at any time. It was a perfect tool for our new status as shut-ins. Close family friends would check in each day and ask if there was something I needed at the store since I could not leave Conner alone due to his fragile health. Our community's support took the burden off of me, the primary caregiver, of repeatedly asking for help. This also reduced my feelings of being overwhelmed and/or isolated. I could focus entirely on my primary role of taking care of my son.

My extended family lived on the East Coast, but that didn't stop them from helping us. My parents paid for a cleaning service after I confided to my dad that my stomach ached just thinking about having to come home from the hospital and worry about the germs lurking at home. Every other Friday, when we were scheduled to return from chemotherapy, the cleaning company came in to do deep disinfecting of our kitchen and bathrooms, vacuum and mop the floors. Since I was away at chemo with Conner, and my husband worked full time and cared for our older son, neither of us had the time to clean or disinfect the house. The peace of mind the cleaning service provided was immeasurable. I later learned there are volunteer groups who provide such services to families (http://www.cleaningforareason.org). My sisters and my mom flew out over their long breaks and vacations to help out as well. My youngest sister, Erin, even helped me re-organize our linen and clothing closets. My mom came out to help right after Conner's shoulder reconstruction and tumor excision surgery. Her experience as a nurse was invaluable.

I recall two friends who visited Conner and me in the hospital just after Halloween. Trying to cheer me up, Vicky exclaimed, "Oh, after Halloween comes Christmas. I love this time of year!"

I responded by lamenting, "Look where we are. I just don't feel like celebrating this year. We'll probably be here anyway. I am just too tired to do Christmas." I know I probably disappointed them, but I couldn't contain my bitterness.

Yet I saw matching smiles cross their faces as Trena and Vicky exclaimed, "What if we brought Christmas to you! We can have our small group set up your Christmas tree and decorate your house. You wouldn't have to do a thing."

The look of utter amazement that crossed my face was thank-you enough for my girlfriends. A month later, their group helped Paul buy an artificial tree (no live plants allowed in the house due to germs), then trimmed it and our whole house. They sent a photo of the house and tree all lit up to Conner and me at the hospital via text on my cell phone. Upon receiving that photo, I cried in our hospital room and shared it with Conner, who nodded and said "Cool!" This was a huge affirmation from him. We couldn't wait to return home to sit by our tree.

Throughout Conner's treatment, long-distance and local friends mailed cards of support, books, DVDs, and games. Their gifts and words of support helped us keep up our spirits on a daily basis.

In addition to the meals our friends made for us, Conner's soccer team, my son Patrick's swim team, and my sister's group of friends back East raised more than $2,000 to use toward meals from DreamDinners.com. You simply log onto the website, select a store near you, preview a menu, and order. You can choose to either prepare the meal at an affiliated store near you or pay extra to have the store employees prepare the meal for you. All meals are made to freeze: then you cook them at home when you are ready to eat them. The company donated the labor and prepared the meals for us. Friends offered to pick up the meals at our neighborhood store and deliver them to our house. I didn't have to prepare a meal for my family, unless I chose, for the entire course of treatment.

These kind acts of service alone gave us hope and a sense of love that lifted us through many dark days. When others reach out to ask what they can do to help, here are some choices to match their abilities with your family's needs. There are so many situations where your friends' different abilities and talents and their freedom from care can be of help to you.

WHAT CAN I DO TO HELP?

For those who want to volunteer their services, here are some suggestions to help you work together to select good options:

- ♥ *Do you like to cook?* Prepare a meal or some baked goods for the family. Remember to keep in mind the family's dietary restrictions and food preferences so your meal will be enjoyed. Don't bring YOUR tuna noodle casserole if the family doesn't like tuna because you think they haven't tried YOUR RECIPE. Use disposable pans and/or paper plates so the family won't have to worry about cleaning dishes or returning them.

- ♥ *Do you love to garden or do yard work?* Offer to mow the lawn, weed, prune, or water the plants—indoor plants, too. The yard and plants are often neglected when families turn their entire focus to caring for their loved ones.

- ♥ *Are you good with animals?* Serving as dog walkers, pet sitters, kitty-litter-box scoopers, small animal cage cleaners, and even foster pet families for pets who need temporary homes while patients undergo treatment or can no longer care for their pets is a wonderful way to help a family. (My son had a pet gecko that needed to be adopted for a year during his chemotherapy and post-chemo because of the salmonella contamination risk to him with his reduced immune system.) Animals are a part of the family and are so therapeutic for the patient and family members during an illness. It is important that they are not forgotten.

♥ ***Are you crafty or enjoy an easy hobby?*** Share your love of a certain skill with the patient, friend, or family member by dropping by to visit the hospital or home to teach or share such skills as crocheting, card-making, sewing, model-building. These quiet activities help occupy fidgety hands and soothe worried minds as the patient gets absorbed in the activity with a friend—you.

♥ ***Do you like to read and/or write?*** Send an affirming card or note to the patient, caregiver, or family members to let them know you are thinking of them. These encouraging messages are invaluable morale boosters during trying times. Reading a soothing passage from a favorite book brings comfort at almost any time. If you can't visit in person, you can record your reading on a smart phone and email the file or place it in Dropbox.com for download onto an e-tablet or other device (audio files are often quite large).

♥ ***Do you have time to offer to wait in the waiting room during appointments, long treatments, or to keep the family company?*** If the patient and/or caregiver desires, you can pray or meditate with them.

♥ ***Do you enjoy taking people on outings?*** Offer to take the caregiver, spouse, or sibling of the patient on an outing. Isolation and burnout are a big risk for these people and time spent just talking when removed from home, however brief, is a big mental health break for all involved.

♥ ***Are you well organized? Do you like to clean?*** Drop by and offer to clean a bathroom, wipe down the refrigerator, mop a kitchen floor. Offer to do some laundry. If you are out running errands, ask the family if they need a specific item at the store or ask for a list of items you can bring them.

2

IT'S OKAY TO CRY

Difficult news is never easy to hear. It can be even more challenging to pass the news along to friends and loved ones. But it is necessary to share a tough diagnosis by communicating honestly. This includes expressing your feelings openly and not getting sidetracked with drama or fear. You and the patient are most likely to be scared at first. That is natural and it's okay. It is better to express these emotions than to mask them with platitudes and saying what you think people want to hear, such as: We are fine; He's going to be okay; Children's Hospital is one of the best in the country; Our surgeon is world famous; We caught it in time! When you share your genuine feelings with others, you break down emotional barriers and let others know you are receptive to their help. A strong bond is then forged.

When our son Conner was first diagnosed with cancer, I went into autopilot. Since our world had been turned upside down, I had to be in control of something. I began barking out orders at home. "Clean this, disinfect that. Who left this mess here? Don't you know Conner is immune compromised?" I was riding around on my broomstick a whole lot! My husband's response was either to do less or to yell back at me. It wasn't pleasant those first few weeks. One evening, Paul finally asked me, "What is wrong?"

"Oh nothing," I said, convincing neither him nor me. So he asked again. I crumbled. "I am afraid our son might die."

Finally, I was able to face the terrible fear I had been stuffing for weeks underneath piles of laundry, disinfectant rags, emails, and CaringBridge blog entries. The man who had been stiff and angry with me was now holding me and drying my eyes. I could only imagine how difficult our son's cancer diagnosis was for Paul, since he had lost his younger brother to a rare kidney disorder at age twenty.

"We can't go there now. We have to be strong for Conner. I am afraid, too, but we are a team and we are in this together, okay?" he said calmly, as he searched my eyes for confirmation.

In that moment, I realized that cancer, not my husband, was the enemy. After that, I didn't feel alone.

Sharing the News

Telling your friends is important. They need to understand your pain so they can reach out to you. Our friend Lisa is a deeply spiritual woman. Her daughter had thyroid cancer a year earlier, and I knew she would be an immediate support for us. When I arrived at the church for our weekly women's Bible study, she started walking toward me and welcomed me as usual. We had known each other for more than twenty years. Immediately, she recognized the pain in my eyes, the heaviness in my gait. Lisa knew something was terribly wrong.

We fell into each other's arms, sobbing together as I shared the terrible news of Conner's almost certain cancer diagnosis. The biopsy was going to be done in less than one week, and the results would be confirmed a week after the procedure. Conner had spent a week sailing the San Juan Islands with her family earlier that summer and had become like a part of the family. That period was also when he first started complaining about his arm pain. I shuddered at the memory.

Lisa wept, because she loved our family and knew what lay ahead for us. I cried out of fear, loss, and pain. Eventually, we sat down and tried to compose ourselves. I noticed the questioning, concerned looks from the other women around us. Lisa was the Bible study leader for more than sixty women. She needed to regain her composure. As a mere participant, I had the luxury of remaining lost in my emotions.

Lisa opened the Bible study by welcoming everyone, made a few general announcements, and then said a prayer. General prayer requests were made and people announced prayers that had been answered from previous meetings. Then Lisa offered a special blessing for Conner's diagnosis, healing, and recovery. Although I wept quietly, I felt comforted by a wonderful cloak of prayer and love. Lisa reminded the group that her daughter, Megan, was still recovering from cancer and was one year in remission. That wasn't the case for some of the people in the room who had experienced the loss of loved ones to other serious diseases, including cancer. I soon realized that I wasn't the only person in need of prayers and knew from the women's shared stories that some prayers were answered, while others went unexplained. In between speaking and leading the group, Lisa returned to the table and held my hand. She offered words of encouragement as a mother who had experienced the similar stabbing fear of cancer. I was lost, yet grateful for the company of my close friend that day.

Have a Good Cry

It may seem obvious, but you need to give yourself permission to have a good cry now and then as you pass through the post-diagnosis period. Some people prefer to cry with a loved one or friend. Others need time to be alone. At times, you will need to do both. However you choose to release your feelings, it is important to admit to yourself that you are going to face sadness and fear. And it is healthy to unleash those feelings in a supportive setting. When your loved one is ill, it is vital for you to be able to vent and express your emotions out of sight of him or her. These tips will help you choose safe outlets for channeling your feelings.

- ♥ Find a good therapist for yourself and/or your family whom you can call regularly or on an as-needed basis during this time. Hospitals, too, can be invaluable assets, with referral lists of support groups and social workers at their disposal.

- ♥ Have a list of names for your core support group handy and make sure they are entered into your contacts lists for your phone and email so you can call, text, email at a moment's notice when you need to connect. Also, be aware that different friends can handle different levels of emotions. You'll find Friend A can go very deep in communicating with you immediately; Friend B will try to make you laugh to forget; and Friend C can't go deep, but will drop everything and come running with a meal and an extra change of clean clothes at a moment's notice. Know, appreciate, and accept each friend's strengths and limitations.

♥ Have a go-to activity and location when you need to cry or get emotional. Think of a happy place that not only gives you shelter while you cry but refreshes you afterward, like a drive, run, or walk to a favorite park, lake, or beach or a walk or with your pet. I would often put on my running shoes and go for a long run where I could let the tears just flow. If getting out of the house is not an option, go to the bathroom, close the door, and run the water to drown out the sound of your crying.

♥ Watch a sad movie by yourself to stimulate a good cry. The release will be just as therapeutic as if you were crying directly about your own losses.

3

What to Say

Knowing what to say to your loved one, family, and friends when delivering life-changing bad news is never easy. Sharing our teenage son's cancer diagnosis with him was something we never imagined we would have to do. Plus, many of us have little experience to guide us. I hope our family's story will help.

Telling Conner

I fidgeted with the small business card in my coat pocket that our surgeon had handed me the day before, his cell phone number scrawled across the bottom in case I had any questions. Impulsively, I decided "Why not?" and called him to learn more. The initial shock of my teenage son's potential cancer diagnosis had worn off, and I was ready to get prepared.

"Just what are we dealing with here, Doctor?" I asked, feeling quite bold after he answered my call. I challenged him to tell me the truth.

"Ewing's Sarcoma," he answered evenly and directly. "It's in the right scapula. Actually, it started in the glenohumeral, or shoulder joint as you refer to it, and grew into the scapula. It has an 80 percent cure rate if it hasn't metastasized. And call me Chappie" he continued, a kind reassurance in his voice.

"*Really?* And you can tell that before doing the biopsy? What gives you the authority to make that call?" I confronted him. I had grown up in a family of doctors and nurses; my physician father had been chairman of neonatology at a large metropolitan university hospital. I wasn't easily intimidated. *How dare he diagnose Conner over the phone and destroy this beautiful day with horrific news? Just who does he think he is?* I thought with indignation.

The professional authority returned to his voice. "Thirty years of diagnostic experience; ten years of *that* as chair and department head of orthopedic oncology surgery at two hospitals." He was most assuredly letting me know just who he was.

"Okay, how big is the tumor, and when will we know if it has metastasized?" I gulped, asking the unthinkable, "What are the chances if it has?"

"It's about the size of a peach or a small orange; we'll know more after the biopsy. But let's think about the 80 percent cure rate, okay? The odds aren't as good if it has metastasized," he explained.

"But what *are* the cure rates if it *has* spread?" I felt stubborn, unable to stop from throwing myself off this cliff.

"Less than 5 percent. But I really don't think this has metastasized. It's too early to worry," he said gravely and continued, "And you're going to need to tell Conner about this as soon as possible."

This instruction was another punch to the gut. "But I don't want to tell him now." I could hear my voice sounding small and childlike.

"You've got to tell him, and the sooner the better. Anything you do—your mood, actions—he's going to sense it and he'll know already. It's the right thing to do." Chappie's voice lowered. He sounded kinder and more thoughtful than he did just minutes earlier on the phone, or when he shared the 50/50 cancer diagnosis yesterday. I knew he was right. Darn it, he was right!

The doctors didn't sugarcoat or hide anything from Conner in the examining room yesterday. Why did I think things would be any different today? "Okay, Chappie, Paul and I will tell him tonight," I exhaled, dreading the ominous task that loomed ahead.

Later that evening, Conner knew something wasn't right when we asked him to join us in the living room after dinner. The kids didn't normally hang out in there. The TV, books, and toys were kept in the family room, and the one room that was kept neat and tidy, with our nicer furniture, was the one room where they weren't usually allowed. Paul was trying to look comfortable in the over-stuffed wingback chair, with his feet propped up on the ottoman. I wasn't nearly as successful; I perched on the edge of the sage couch and hugged a big floral pillow to me as a buffer.

"Hey, Mom . . . Dad." Conner greeted us as his eyebrows rose slightly in consternation. He began shifting his weight from one oversized, tennis-shoed foot to another. "Sooo . . . what's going on?" His teenage curiosity was getting the better of him.

"Heeey, Conner," I answered far too cheerfully. It gave us away. He saw right through us, so we just got down to business.

"Conner, we've got something we need to talk to you about," his father began.

"Yeah, I figured that, with you and Mom camped out in here," Conner joked thinly.

"Come sit down." Paul gestured toward the couch.

"No, Dad, I think I'd rather stand," Conner replied, probably realizing that whatever we had to say, it wasn't going to be good.

"Conner, your mom talked to your doctor today and he told us that you've got cancer." The words cut through the air like a steel blade.

"Yeah, Dad, I figured that." Conner swallowed hard and looked down as he shuffled his feet.

"Let me explain, Hon." I could hear the anguish in Paul's voice as he tried to tell Conner what no father or parent should ever have to tell their child or loved one. "Your surgeon believes you've got Ewing's Sarcoma. It's a very rare form of bone cancer. There's a tumor that has grown into your scapula and that's what has been causing all the pain." Paul paused and drew in a deep breath as he continued. "There's a good cure rate—75 to 80 percent—if it hasn't spread. We'll know more after the biopsy and when they remove the tumor."

Conner stood before us. His straight, sandy blond hair swept to the side, framing his handsome face and questioning hazel eyes. He stood 5 feet 2 inches, with long, lanky limbs and oversized adolescent feet that were fixed to the floor. We tried to read his face for emotion and waited for him to say something, anything.

"Well that just sucks," he said grimly, showing a dark anger that tore at my heart. He began to shift back and forth. I could see his running shoes moving forward, then backward, as if he wanted to run away, but where?

I attempted to respond to his anger with a call to battle, as I swallowed my fears. "Yes, it does suck, Conner. But we are going to fight this with everything we can . . . together."

Paul added, "We'll know more when we go back to the hospital this week for the pre-op appointment for the biopsy and then after the biopsy, too. Do you have any questions, Buddy?" I could tell Paul needed to reassure our son, yet felt helpless. What else could we do?

I continued to search Conner's face. There was a haunted look in his eyes, his jaw clenched tight. I realized that my son was withdrawing deep within himself. Little did I understand then that his retreat would be for self-preservation. Our pre-cancer Conner would not emerge again for at least another two years. I wanted desperately to rush over and embrace our son. Yet I knew and respected his need for space to process this staggering news.

"Conner do you need a hug?" I asked, rising quickly to be with him.

"No, Mom, but you look like you could use one," he said with a slight grin and pain in his voice. He wrapped his arms around me and we hugged tightly, standing together as one until Paul joined us. We clung together as a family and braced for the coming storm.

When you have tough news to deliver such as a diagnosis of a potentially fatal illness, it's best to speak the truth. Yet "truth" varies for each family. We were given the option to know our prognosis: some people would rather not know. It's a personal choice. You need to make these decisions as a family and weigh the pros and cons of being told the odds of survival. You'll want to find the best time to share the information with immediate family and/or loved ones. Then, as soon as you can, reach out to your larger network of friends and community.

Becky's Hair

One day during one of our check-in phone conversations during her chemotherapy treatments, my friend Becky, who was fighting breast cancer, told me she was going to lose her hair. Too quick to want to fix things, I interjected, "Oh, Becky, you know it will grow back."

I immediately realized it was an insensitive thing to say.

With an uncharacteristic gasp in her voice, she snapped, "I didn't need to hear that, Kathy! This is hard for me and don't want to be . . . bald."

"I'm sorry, I'm sorry! I'm so stupid, please forgive me," I fumbled for words, trying to fix the mess I had made of our conversation. I was red with shame, knowing I had hurt my friend's feelings. This was the close friend I thought was tough and strong, whose feelings weren't easily hurt. *I'm such a jerk!* I thought to myself.

There was a slight pause on the other end of the phone as Becky took a moment to clear her throat before she continued. "Hey, you didn't realize what you were saying. There are cool hats and kerchiefs. It could be okay," she offered. Always quick to forgive, a little humor returned to her voice, a sign of her forgiveness for my well-meaning mistake.

Knowing what to say in difficult situations is uncomfortable for a patient, a caregiver, and a friend. Armed beforehand with some helpful ideas and tips, you may be better prepared to offer reassurance or consolation to those dealing with the impact of a serious illness.

What to Say

Our account shows how we shared a cancer diagnosis with our teenage son. How one might deliver such news to a young child versus an adult will vary greatly.

Years ago, a close friend who lost her son to chemical addiction told me the hardest part of grief was when people you know remain silent and say nothing. I suggested that perhaps people didn't know what to say and asked what she'd like people to say to her. She told me it would be comforting to hear "I am sorry this happened" and to know people cared and acknowledged her loss.

There's nothing that can ever rescue or bring back a loved one, but a soothing word of support can go a long way and be a healing balm. Remembering my friend's words, I try to say something empathetic to those going through hard times. I also reflect back on how welcome kind words were to us while our son was sick. Sometimes a sympathetic look, hug, or touch was equally comforting.

If, however, you are having a hard time finding the right words to say, hospital gift shops have greeting cards with a variety of sentiments that you can sign and mail or hand-deliver to your loved one. I used to leave little notes on my husband and older son's pillows before leaving for multiple-day hospital chemotherapy stays with Conner. An encouraging word, a kind gesture or statement from you, is an incredible gift to someone in crisis. By reaching out in this way, you let someone know he or she is not alone and has your support.

What follows are suggestions for positive things to say to anyone facing a serious illness or loss, as well as a list of things to avoid saying.

What to Say

- ♥ "I am so sorry this has happened to you and your family."
- ♥ "I can make meals for your family, run errands, or shop for groceries for you. Tell me what you need."
- ♥ "I am here to listen. If you need a friend to talk to, call me anytime." (Be sure to follow up with email, voicemail, or text).
- ♥ "Take it one day at a time. It'll help you avoid feeling so overwhelmed."
- ♥ "You are in our thoughts and prayers."
- ♥ "You will get through this." (This is most convincing coming from someone who has been through a similar experience.)
- ♥ "If you ever want to talk this out with a professional, I can refer you to a very thoughtful therapist.

Having weathered a serious illness with my son, as well as with several close friends, I asked those who were fighting to survive and their caregivers what people should avoid saying. Yet, what offends one person may not offend another. These are just suggestions, written to help you understand the caregiver and family's perspective and perhaps avoid some potential pitfalls. Read them with a measure of subjectivity.

Don't feel bad if you find yourself inadvertently making a blunder. Just apologize and move forward. It is better to be a friend who is caring and present than one who is absent and unavailable.

What Not to Say

- ♥ "Do you think he/she will survive this?"
- ♥ "And I thought I was having a bad day." or "I could never do what you are doing." (Nobody wants to be reminded of his or her misfortune or pitied.)

♥ "Does it hurt?" or "Aren't you scared?" (This is as helpful as picking a scab.)

♥ "Don't worry. Your hair will grow back. Meantime, you can just wear a hat or a wig. They make such great ones now; nobody will ever tell."

♥ "Wheelchairs and prosthetics are almost like you are walking on your own." (This minimizes the pain the person is feeling and brushes over the depth of someone's loss.)

♥ "Is this cancer hereditary? What do you think might have caused this—exposure to chemicals or some food?" (Asking someone to speculate about what caused an illness such as cancer is foolish. Even doctors seldom have these answers.)

♥ "Aren't you lucky you're a stay-at-home mom and have time to take care of him?" (Cancer parents never feel lucky. More appropriate to commend such a mom for her loving strength and devotion.)

♥ "I feel so bad for you." (Nobody wants to be pitied.)

♥ "It was so hard when my dad had cancer." (Try not to shift the focus to you and the difficulties you have experienced.)

4

UNDERSTANDING
YOUR LOVED ONE

How the loved one who has a serious illness interacts with the immediate caregiver versus the community and extended friends and family will differ by individual. The caregiver needs to understand the patient's immediate needs intimately, because he or she will serve as buffer and advocate between the patient and the outside world. If the caregiver is not careful in selecting who provides help and how much of it the loved one receives, well-meaning people may do more harm than good. The patient's personality and temperament will give the caregiver clues about who and what are appropriate.

For example, some patients are social. They'll want lots of friends to visit them. Others are quiet, need their space, and may only want one or two very close friends to stop by. But every patient will be more tired than they were used to being when healthy. It is up to the caregiver to screen the amount of visitors and the timing of the visits so the loved one receives the proper rest and also keeps to his or her treatment and or medication schedule. This will vary between home and hospital stays—and will change as treatments shift. What follows are the new rules and protocol we determined would work best for our son's recovery.

Our New Rules for Conner

- ♥ Since Conner was no longer able to attend school, he was home-schooled by school-assigned tutors and by hospital tutors while an in-patient.

- ♥ Conner was not allowed to be near anyone with cold or flu symptoms. If a caregiver had symptoms, he or she had to wear a surgical mask and surgical gloves when anywhere near him.

- ♥ Conner had to remain within a 60-mile radius of Seattle Children's Hospital at all times. All family vacations where therefore canceled for the next ten months.

- ♥ Conner could not be left alone for more than thirty minutes due to his fragile health and the necessity of maintaining his central line, a catheter that is surgically placed near his heart and used to administer chemotherapy drugs and take blood samples. It needed to be flushed daily and the dressing changed weekly.

- ♥ Conner could no longer eat at buffet-style restaurants, consume food left out longer than two hours, or eat raw or unpasteurized food (sushi and blue cheese, which were among his favorite foods, were not permitted in his diet) or leftovers, nor could he consume any food past its sell date.

- ♥ Conner's braces had to be removed from his teeth immediately as the mouth sores that would develop during chemotherapy would make orthodontic treatment unbearable.

- ♥ The new, cool loft-bed we had just bought for Conner needed to be removed from his room and replaced with a more practical twin bed that he could access more easily.

- ♥ Conner had to consume 60 ounces of fluids daily as well as 1,800 calories of food to keep up his strength.

- ♥ Conner's temperature had to be taken every day: if his temperature rose to 99°F, we had to call the Oncology Unit; if it exceeded 100°F, he would be admitted to the hospital immediately.

Given all his new restrictions, we had one angry, sullen thirteen-year-old whose two parents and two siblings tried their best to make him happy. Most teenage boys are beginning to cut the apron strings and assert their independence at this age. It's a healthy stage of development, albeit one that stresses out parents, and there is much debate over how much and what type of independence to grant a teen. But to be returned to toddler status at almost fourteen years of age was abysmal for Conner and he let us know of his outrage in no uncertain terms.

Care-sitters or friends who dropped by to watch Conner while I ran an errand or took a quick break were often ignored as he holed up in his room. It was as if doing this made him feel he really wasn't being watched and that he didn't need any help or pity. I made excuses for his sullen behavior, but it was often awkward. Despite the fact that people wanted to help, Conner was angry that his freedom had been stolen from him, and he wasn't in a mood to show them appreciation.

Conner had two close friends, who still visited regularly during his cancer treatment. Matthew and Jason were childhood friends who were as comfortable with Conner with cancer as they had been with Conner pre-cancer. Right after Conner's central line was inserted, he was wary of how Matthew and Jason would treat him. Many kids looked at him as if they'd seen a ghost and just stopped coming over. When his friends arrived, he just had to show them his central line. "Hey guys, check this out," he said as he lifted his shirt to show the tubing that was taped over his heart and snaked like thin rubber hose halfway down his chest. Jason merely shrugged and said, "Yeah, so, let's go check out that new video game you got." The three boys bounded up the stairs. Seeing how natural his close friends were with him, I knew Conner was going to be okay.

As caregiver, I let people know their support was helpful and explained why my son was withdrawn. I also had to play gatekeeper and shield Conner from visits that he didn't want while he was adjusting to his diagnosis.

One friend offered to have her family shave their heads in solidarity for Conner. This gesture would have been most welcome by some, but the extra attention mortified my son, who, when the time came, just wanted to have his head shaved in his hospital room, quietly grieve his hair loss, and put on his favorite beanie without comment. Some patients eventually overcome their reclusiveness. My son didn't and, for the most part, wanted to remain alone during most of his treatment.

The Seahawks Come to Visit

Even though Conner and I were closely tied day in and day out during the treatment process, I needed to learn that I did not completely understand what my son was going through.

It was close to Father's Day. Seahawks and Mariners players were visiting Seattle Children's Hospital as part of their yearly family-building tradition. Our older son, Patrick, came to visit his brother and was excited to be there for a visit from a famous Seahawks football player and one of the Sea Gals cheerleaders.

"Hey, Conner! The Sea Gals are here! Don't you want to have them come in and say hi to you?" Patrick egged Conner on with a wink.

Conner, now almost eight months into chemotherapy, grumbled under his blanket, his back turned to both of us. "Go away! Just leave me alone!" he said. Conner burrowed deeper into his hospital bed.

I felt sorry for Patrick, who was really trying to engage his brother and who would desperately have liked some special attention, too. I tried to entice Conner, "Conner, the Seahawks are here. They'll sign your autograph, and they've got posters and lots of swag." But it wasn't working.

"Leave me alone. I said I don't *CARE*," Conner responded angrily.

I thought it would be good for both the boys to have a visit from someone famous. I started begging, "But Conner, Patrick is here and he'd like to see them, too. Don't you want them to come in?"

"Patrick can go see them if he wants. *I don't CARE!*" Conner yelled. He was furious.

"You're killing me here!" Patrick growled and walked out of the room, dejected.

Patrick was trying to bond with his younger brother and getting nowhere. With just Conner and I left in the room, I tried to explain, "You know, he was only trying to help and you're being a little selfish here. Would it be that hard to have a visit with the Seahawks? Your brother wanted to do something together with you, and it would cheer you both up."

Conner rolled over and mustered as much strength as he could. Groaning, he sat up in bed and met my gaze. "Mom, look at me."

I did. I saw my beautiful baldheaded son, fighting to the very end of chemotherapy, strong, frail, brave, and honest.

"I'm sick, pale, bald, I want to throw up, and you want a Sea Gal to come in and see me?" His voice wavered, "The only reason they want to see me is because I have cancer. Not to see me. I don't want anybody to see me, I don't feel well. Please leave me alone, Mom, please. . . ." Tears welled up in his eyes, and he swiped awkwardly with the back of his hand at a stray tear.

I finally understood. He wanted those people to visit him when he was himself, not the shell he was now. He didn't want pity or sympathy. He just wanted to deal with his sickness in his own humble, private way and be allowed to do so. I realized there are many ways to travel this path, and all must be respected. Conner's cancer journey was not about me or his brother or anyone else, but about him. I needed to acknowledge and accept that.

Before I had a chance to comfort him, the Seahawks player appeared in our doorway, a huge god of a man with muscles that rippled through his jersey and long golden tresses that just grazed his shoulders. He asked to come in and visit Conner. It was all I could do not to invite him in, but I was Conner's gatekeeper now.

I stood up, swallowed hard, and explained, "My son doesn't feel well today and doesn't want any visitors; but thank you for coming anyway."

The powerful-looking Seahawk bowed his head. There was deep respect tinged with sorrow in his voice as he spoke: "I completely understand, Ma'am, but please . . . may I leave this poster for him?" I thanked him as I accepted his gift. I then stepped back into Conner's room, knowing I had honored Conner's wishes instead of trying to press my own on him.

Take Your Caring Cues from the Patient

It can be very easy for people to get swept up in helping. Although such help is well-intended, it can be counterproductive if one's own agenda overshadows the desires and needs of the patient. Do not expect anything in return for your loving care. The person battling illness is all-consumed by his struggle to survive. By understanding the patient, foremost, and what he is dealing with—his symptoms, diagnosis, and prognosis—you will be best able to understand his perspective and provide effective help. For example, if you are dealing with an immune-compromised patient, you'll understand why you need to stay away if you have any cold symptoms, even though you really want to see him. You will send a card instead, communicating your ongoing care without risking the patient's health.

Also, when you are helping, you'll want to just focus on the task at hand and not worry too far into the future. If you know the patient tends to be quiet and would rather just have someone come and sit rather than talk, pack up your conversation and leave it at home. Try to value the comfort that your silent presence offers him. And if the patient is suffering, do your best to be present for him, and do not show your own fear and dismay. Love is what he needs most from you in that moment. And calm reassurance. You are there for him, not for you. Make your caring as selfless as you possibly can.

By availing yourself of self-care, support systems, an occasional good cry, and some other techniques this book provides, you will be strong enough to give the patient the individualized help he needs to fight his illness and regain a sense of wholeness.

Ways to Understand the Patient

- ♥ Do some research on the patient's diagnosis. Try to understand the magnitude of the information he has been told and is attempting to digest. It will help you empathize better.

- ♥ Listen to the patient and do not interject your own advice and/or agenda. Instead, try to hear what the patient is saying. Some may need to complain, others will want to tell you exactly what is wrong, while some people won't say much. Yet pay attention to body language—a sigh, facial expression, nervous tapping, or even avoidance speaks volumes as to what is going on within.

- ♥ Spend time with the patient so you don't miss out on opportunities for him to volunteer his feelings. He is scared, trying to be brave, and wants to keep things as "normal" as possible. However, over time, telltale glimpses into his true feelings and emotions do slip out.

- ♥ With young and/or uncommunicative patients, hospital workers use charts with faces on a spectrum from 1 to 10 called the "pain chart." The chart starts with a no-pain smiley face and ends with a miserable grimace. This helps care providers and medical personnel effectively gauge patient pain levels. Also, emoticons and similar stickers and magnets are very effective on a day-to-day basis in helping a patient express how he feels at any given moment.

♥ Using a storybook for young patients, books and DVDs at any age as a catalyst and vehicle for discussion can also encourage the patient to discuss his feelings. Remember, his feelings will change and evolve during treatment and over the course of the disease/illness, with ups and downs that mirror successes and setbacks.

5

How to Bring Home to the Hospital

When my son Conner first started treatment for his cancer, my awkward efforts to help him made me stick out as a newbie. I juggled the bundles and bags that spilled out from the sides of Conner's wheelchair from the parking lot to our hospital room. Other times, when Conner could walk, we'd pull the hospital-issued red plastic wagons stacked with luggage.

We attempted to sleep on stiff, scratchy hospital linens.

I had an embarrassing wake-up call when six doctors and interns showed up for morning rounds, and I was clad in a thin pajama top that didn't cover quite all of me. I needed to find a twenty-four-hour sweat suit I could sleep and wake in within seconds.

I made unsuccessful food runs all over the hospital campus at 2 a.m., seeking whatever elusive morsel Conner craved. Do you know how hard it is to find a bean and cheese taco at 2 in the morning? We ate terrible food, suspecting there was something better.

Around the start of Conner's third round of chemotherapy, I decided to create a list of what to bring to the hospital. We'd settled in. Later that night we got a roommate, a young man who was admitted after we had fallen asleep. He wasn't doing very well. He'd thrown up his feeding tube, and the nurses had come in to help his mother clean him up and decide what to do. I prayed silently that

Conner wouldn't wake up and hear the sounds of this boy sobbing and retching. I also prayed for this mother and young man whom I hadn't yet met.

When I woke the next morning, I noticed my neighbor Diane, the boy's mother. We'd met in the hallway that night as I went to get Conner a snack. Diane had a soft faux leopard print blanket on her lap and a small portable reading lamp attached to the chair (this was before backlit e-readers).

"You look so comfortable," I observed admiringly.

"Have you noticed how *dark* it is in here? The hospital-issue blankets and pillows aren't comfortable either, so we pack ours in from home. It's so much better and David appreciates it," Diane explained.

"They let you bring stuff from home?" I asked in amazement. "Nobody told me."

"Sure they do. It makes a hospital room feel more like home—and having your own games, books, and craft items helps to pass the time. Who wants to sit and read in the dark? When I turn on the light, David whines and makes me turn it off." She gestured toward his bed and frowned sadly. "The light just bothers him when he's feeling sick and nauseated. This way, I can still read, knit, do my crossword puzzles, whatever, and not disturb him." Diane smiled softly. She was full of good information.

"No kidding! I'm bringing in my stuff next time!" I vowed.

One morning after a trip to the family center for a shower, I spilled soap and a large bottle of shampoo on the floor after jamming my arm into a bag so stuffed with clothes that my T-shirt fell into a puddle. I decided I needed a better system. I noticed that other parents wore flip-flops and Crocs and had brought tiny Ziploc bags filled with single-use toiletries that fit in a single tote bag. As well, many of the women had neatly tied their hair into ponytails or buns. I realized my days of trying to be the perfect PTA mom who never left the house without full makeup and matching outfit were over.

Trying to play a board game with Conner from his hospital bed was also challenging. We set up the game with pieces on top of his tiny bed tray, placing the board's fulcrum on the center of the tray. Midway into the game, his nurse entered the room to take Conner's vital signs, and we had to remove the board game quickly without scattering all the pieces. I began bringing travel games instead. Their miniature boards and magnetic pieces were terrific for adapting to small spaces and making quick transitions.

I wanted to bring pictures from home of Conner's pre-cancer days to tape to the hospital room walls and cupboards or to pin to his bulletin board to remind us and him of who he was before cancer. I felt sure these images would create hope for the after-treatment time ahead. I had a new project!

My mind was clicking with ideas and information about ways to bring comfort and touches of the familiar to our hospital room. The list of what I could bring to the hospital also included some convenient items that stream-lined our stays.

What to Bring to the Hospital

- ♥ Bring a pillow or small throw blanket from home for you and the patient. The familiar pattern, color, and comfortable fabric will cheer you during your stay.

- ♥ Pack comfortable all-purpose clothing such as sweatpants, T-shirts, or a jogging suit. Your sleep and wake cycles will vary, so being dressed in clothing that works 24/7 is helpful.

- ♥ Roll-away luggage (carry-on size) is easier to transport from your car to the hospital room and from your room to shower areas than an over-the-shoulder bag.

- ♥ Pack travel-sized toiletries that can easily be disposed of when you've finished using them and that take up minimal space. (Most drugstores have a special section filled with a big selection of these mini-toiletries.)

- ♥ Don't forget to pack a separate bag for your dirty laundry and flip-flops to wear in the hospital shower.

- ♥ At home, have a pre-packed bag with a change of clothes and toiletries that is ready to go at a moment's notice. Position it by the front door at all times for those unexpected hospital visits.

- ♥ Pack an activity bag with travel-sized games. They're great for tight spaces in the hospital. They fit easily on hospital bed tables and the magnetized pieces don't scatter. Also, consider games that pack up quickly when you need to stop for a procedure or the patient is tired. Good options are handheld games, reading materials, Sudoku, crossword puzzles, and iPads and tablets. Card games, Bananagrams, and schoolwork when applicable are also fun activities.

♥ You never know when someone on chemo will be hungry, and you don't want to miss that brief opportunity to give comfort. If the hospital doesn't provide an in-room refrigerator, keep a small cooler stocked with your child's favorite beverages and snacks. (Ask first about allergies, special dietary restrictions, and hospital rules.) Freezer packs to keep food and drink cool can be stored and rotated from the family kitchen freezer.

♥ Some food ideas include peanut butter and jelly sandwiches, cheese cubes, grapes, salted nuts, and potato chips. Chewing gum may help take away the chemo aftertaste (Conner preferred mint and sometimes sour fruit flavors). Pack snacks for yourself, too. You can save a small fortune by not frequenting the hospital cafeteria and cafes: you'll have bills to pay after treatment is over. Also, when you're staying 24 hours, hospital food venues may close at 7 p.m.

♥ Putting up pictures or small posters and cards from home can add a familiar and homey touch to the hospital room. These pictures of favorite places and loved ones remind us of better times and happier places. It can also be a catalyst for conversation with health-care providers and visitors.

♥ Handwork such as knitting, crocheting, needlepoint, and cross-stitch are wonderful ways to pass the time while the patient is sleeping or otherwise occupied. They will calm nervous hands and occupy your mind with something more positive than worry.

♥ Remember to say please and thank you to everyone you meet and who cares for your patient, even if you're under tremendous stress. The hospital staff wants to help, and a little appreciation from you goes a long way in showing your gratitude for their care. If he or she is able, encourage your loved one to say please and thank you as well.

6

FOOD FOR THE SOUL

When a crisis hits, I have found that food brings people comfort. Families will gather around a meal, friends will sit and visit over a cup of coffee, beverage, and snacks; food will be offered and savored. Fortunately, the act of cooking and baking has always brought me joy, so I am able to share my gifts when needed. Years before our struggles with Conner's illness, a close family friend was quite ill with breast cancer, and it was time for us to help. I wanted to teach my children to be a part of the giving experience.

We Help a Friend by Cooking

The week after we learned just how sick our friend Becky was and that her family was going to need help, I got busy doing some of the *something* that Becky and her family needed. "Okay, Kids, we're going to start making meals for Becky and her family," I announced to my children at dinner one evening.

"Why? What's wrong with Becky?" my nine-year-old daughter asked, her big green eyes opened wide as she awaited answers.

"Well, she has cancer and the chemo treatments are making her too weak and sick to cook dinner for her family now, so she needs our help," I explained. "What kinds of food do you think they'd like to eat?" I asked, trying to steer the conversation away from the cancer and toward something more positive, like favorite dishes and yummy food.

"I know what cancer is," Jennifer called out. She was seated directly across from me at the dinner table. Jennifer was quite precocious and caught me off guard. She would not be diverted and continued, "It's bad and it attacks your body. People die from it. Is Becky going to die?" Jennifer could always get right to the heart of the matter in a millisecond.

"No, Becky is not going to die," I laughed, trying to convince myself of this as much as my daughter. I rolled my eyes and made a silly face to lighten the mood and get the boys to laugh as well. "Yes, it's serious, but she's being seen at University Hospital, where some of the best doctors in the world are treating her. She's going to fight it and get better."

"Okay, so what do you want us to make?" Jennifer responded, seeming unconvinced by my assurances, but wanting to move the conversation along.

"How about baked ziti and 'impossible pie'? You guys love those, right?" I chattered, grateful the topic had changed.

"Yeah, yummy," cheered Patrick, his bright brown eyes shining and chubby, round cheeks flushed as he smiled wide. He loved to eat and loved good cooking even more.

The next day, I lined up three aluminum pans on the kitchen counter, one in front of each of my children, who were perched upon waist-high stools. In order, there was Jennifer, nine; Patrick, five; and Conner, who was then three. I smiled as I looked at my eager assembly line, their short legs and feet dangling over the sides of the stools, none tall enough yet to touch the floor.

"Okay, we're going to begin making baked ziti. First, you take some spoonfuls of tomato sauce and cover the bottom of your pan." I held out the pan of sauce, as each child took a spoonful or two to spread on the inside of their aluminum pan. Conner needed help. He and I held the spoon together as I helped him pour the sauce. Then we added a layer of ziti and covered it with grated cheddar. We repeated the layering, with the children having the most fun sprinkling the cheese. When we finished, everyone grabbed a few slivers of tangy grated cheddar for themselves, a reward for a job well done.

Every few days, we'd work together on different casseroles for Becky. As well, we sometimes added a dish for other friends who needed an extra meal to help when a new baby arrived or when the flu hit and parents were too ill or busy with sick children to cook. The children and I would talk about how our meal would help the family it was going to. And always, we'd talk about how Becky was brave and busy fighting cancer. It was my hope to instill in my children a sense of compassion for others, compassion that we as a family would later need and receive in ways that we could not possibly anticipate at the time.

As time passed, I checked in with Becky on almost a daily basis. One afternoon while I was talking on the phone with her, she threw me off guard by asking me for a favor. "Kathy, would you take a picture of the kids making those meals for me? I can just see their little faces all lined up, their expressions as they are busy making food. That would be such a gift, more than the meal itself. Promise you'll do that for me?"

I heard a slight pause on the other end of the phone and, at first, I just didn't know what to say. "Sure, of course," I answered. I hadn't really thought about what we had been doing as being noteworthy and was touched that she wanted to capture the memory in photos. She thought much more deeply and got to the real heart behind an act faster than anyone I knew.

"You're teaching those kids well. They'll never forget this and neither will I," she continued and mentioned some more of my children's kind attributes that she appreciated.

But my mind became a fog, because I was about to cry. I didn't like her talking like that. Why are we talking about forgetting? I thought. It sounded so final, as if there would be an ending to her story, as if she might not be around to tell them herself, or to see them fully grown one day. No, this cannot be happening, it won't happen, I yelled desperately within.

Although Becky didn't survive, the comfort we provided her with food prepared lovingly was a lasting lesson for our family. When my own son became sick years later, I remembered what to do and I believe he did, too.

Nutrition and Caregiving

Providing good nutrition plays a major role in caregiving. The patient needs to keep well-nourished to maintain strength, and this can become difficult when he is nauseated or on a trying treatment schedule. Eventually, our son had to be given an NG Tube (naso-gastric feeding tube that was inserted up through his nostril and went down his throat and into his stomach). Protein-rich formula was then pumped into his stomach at a rate of 2 ml per hour, twenty-four hours a day, to ensure he received the nutrients he required. He had to carry a small backpack called a Kangaroo Pack at all times that contained both the battery-powered pump and the liquid protein pouch. Every twenty-four hours, the battery needed to be recharged and the pouch refilled with cold, premeasured formula. Some patients receive a stoma or port through their stomach or have other methods of receiving nutrition intravenously, while others are on a very restricted diet. Whatever those limits are, it is up to the caregiver to work within those parameters to extend some level of comfort to the patient.

To help Conner keep his weight up, I cooked and baked his favorite foods on demand. I remember his body craving just what he needed as he demanded slabs of fresh lean steak, razor-thin slices of green apples, and crisp lettuce with dressing at odd times. His holiday favorites were iced sugar cookies. They took a lot of preparation, but were worth the work: even with a sour stomach and pounding headache, Conner devoured them enthusiastically. I was glad he ate them because he needed every extra calorie I could get into him! It was also Conner's idea that I bring them to the hospital and share them with his doctors and nurses. I added hospital tutors, dietitians, and people who cleaned our room to the list of recipients. I thought his idea was wonderful and demonstrated that my children understood about helping others and showing appreciation. I was encouraged that Conner had listened. I thought back to all the meals we had prepared for Becky and how she had said I had taught my children well. *Yes perhaps I had and now it was coming full circle,* I thought with a bittersweet smile.

I also made a batch of snickerdoodles, Conner's other favorite cookie, for the surgical team that would be performing his lifesaving tumor removal and shoulder reconstruction surgery. My friend Jeanne had me attach a poem she had written one sleepless night to the box of cookies: "When you don your mask and glove, don't forget our precious gift from above . . ." The poem and the cookies would give our surgical team all the inspiration they needed, I thought to myself.

Throughout Conner's illness, we found many opportunities to share and receive food. We even learned a special homeopathic remedy from a single ingredient quite by accident. Conner and Patrick's former first-grade teacher, Ms. Gavaghan, came to visit us in the hospital one afternoon. Her wonderful Irish lilt, gentle tinkling laughter, and overall warmth put everyone at ease. Ms. Gavaghan pulled out some homemade pizzelle cookies from a small paper sack.

She had made an entire stack of them that morning just for Conner. These Italian waffle cookies were thin and crispy, looking like a cross between a waffle and a snowflake, and had an anise or black licorice flavor. Conner perked up from his pile of sagging pillows and throw blankets in his bed and asked if he could try one. I was pleased when he finished the entire cookie and asked for another. It was his first solid food of the day.

"These are really good. Thank you. They're light, not greasy or heavy on my stomach and the taste of them—it just settles my nausea," Conner remarked, quite surprised, and raised his eyebrows.

"Really?" I responded with pleasure. He had uttered a complete sentence, another first again for the day.

"Ms. Gavaghan, you might be onto something here." I smiled and gave her a hug. I was rewarded with another round of her laughter. I also thought these cookies and their soothing effect on Conner's stomach might be something I needed to share with our friends on the rest of the oncology floor.

After Ms. Gavaghan left, I visited our young neighbor in the bed just beyond the curtain and offered him and his mother a pizzelle cookie. They were from China. He was only eight and was being treated for brain cancer. His mother was fascinated by this new and different cookie. I explained that it was an Italian pizzelle cookie and that my son had found it soothing for his sick stomach. She smiled and graciously accepted my gift. I continued to visit other "friends" I knew along the floor, including nurses I had come to know on a first-name basis, sharing our new-found cookie discovery.

While it is important to have a repertoire of comfort foods or go-to recipes that will be appetizing for both the patient and caregiver, we were warned not to have Conner eat his favorite foods after his first chemotherapy treatment or he would thereafter associate it with being sick and might never want to eat that food again. Although Conner does not like me comparing chemo nausea to morning sickness during pregnancy, the effect of eating certain foods at the wrong time can be similar. Aversion to that food can be permanent. Conner ate Salisbury steak after his first round of chemotherapy. On day two of treatment, he got sick and tasted "minty meat" for days. It was four months before he would eat ground beef of any kind and, to this day, he will not eat meatloaf or Salisbury steak. You'll want to create a list of comforting, tried-and-true favorites to cook or bake when your loved one is ready. The recipes that follow are a few of Conner's favorites to get you started. You may wish to consult many recently published nutritious and antioxidant-rich recipes that have been shown to strengthen a patient's immune system and support healing. We made our meals and treats for Conner based on caloric and comfort needs, which research has shown also provide healing in cancer patients.

RECIPES FOR A FEW COMFORT FOODS

BAKED ZITI

Makes 10–12 servings

If you need to make a hearty, delicious meal for dinner and don't have the time to prepare a lasagna, this recipe is perfect. Don't worry: it's just as delicious!

½ C chopped onion

2–3 garlic cloves, minced

3 T olive oil

½ lb ground beef

½ lb ground pork sausage (spicy or mild)

3 16 oz cans tomato sauce

1 6 oz can tomato paste

3 T red cooking wine

3 T chopped parsley

Salt and pepper to taste (we like crushed red pepper)

1 lb package of penne or ziti pasta

8 oz ricotta cheese

2 C shredded cheddar cheese

2 C shredded mozzarella cheese

1 C shredded parmesan cheese

To make the marina sauce with meat:

1. Sauté the onion and garlic in the olive oil until onions are just translucent and garlic is brown on the edges. Set aside.

2. Brown the ground beef and pork sausage and drain excess fat.

3. Mix the cooked onion and garlic with the meat.

4. Pour the tomato sauce and paste into a large high-sided skillet and add the browned meat mixture. Simmer on low for 45 minutes, stirring occasionally.

5. Add the cooking wine, parsley, salt, and pepper. (Always taste your sauce to see if it needs a little more spice. Remember, it is your sauce!)

Assembling the pasta dish: Preheat oven to 350°F.

6. While the sauce simmers, bring about 2 quarts of water to a boil, add pasta, and cook until al dente (firm and slightly chewy). (Follow the timing instructions on the pasta packaging.) Drain and set pasta aside.

7. Grease a 9 x 13-inch pan or baking dish and cover the bottom of the pan with 1/3 of the meat sauce. Sprinkle the sauce with a layer of cheddar, mozzarella, and Parmesan and dot with ricotta cheese (about 1/3). Top the cheese with a layer of the pasta noodles. Cover the noodles with another layer of meat sauce, cheeses, and noodles. If you have enough ingredients remaining, repeat the layering; end with a layer of meat sauce and cheese.

8. Cover the pan with aluminum foil and bake for 30 minutes. Remove foil and bake for another 15 minutes, until the cheese on top bubbles and browns. (You may want to place a baking sheet with side edges beneath the pan just in case it bubbles over slightly.)

~

SNICKERDOODLE COOKIES

Makes 18–24 cookies

My sister Erin and great friend Jeanne have told me I make the best snickerdoodles. Thanks, guys! I also learned they were my son's favorite cookie during his chemotherapy. The cinnamon in the cookie seemed to soothe his sour stomach. We made a batch for his surgical team as an added good measure. They were quite grateful and so were we!

1/2 C (1 cube) softened butter
1/2 C vegetable shortening
1 1/2 C sugar
2 eggs

$2^{3}/_{4}$ C flour
2 tsp cream of tartar
1 tsp baking soda
$^{1}/_{4}$ tsp salt
2 T sugar
2 tsp ground cinnamon

Preheat oven to 400°F.

1. Place dry ingredients (except the 2 T sugar and 2 tsp cinnamon) in a small mixing bowl and whisk until blended. Set aside.

2. In a separate larger bowl, using a mixer, cream butter, shortening, and sugar until fluffy. Add eggs one at a time and beat until blended after each addition.

3. Add dry ingredients to creamed mixture and stir until well blended.

4. Place remaining sugar and cinnamon into a small bowl and mix.

5. Roll the dough into teaspoon-sized balls, one at a time, and roll the balls in the cinnamon mixture until well coated. Place about an inch apart on a baking sheet and bake for 8–10 minutes. When done, cookies should have a slightly cracked surface and be moist and chewy within. Remove cookies from the oven and let set on the baking sheet for a minute or two. Remove and cool on a rack.

TIP: I find placing the cookie sheet on a preheated baking stone makes the best cookies—cookies bake evenly and the bottoms don't over-brown.

~

ICED ROLLED SUGAR COOKIES

Makes 18–24 cookies

What began as Christmas cookies soon became an all-time favorite tradition for family and friends. I use a big assortment of cookie cutters to make these cookies for nearly any occasion. My Aunt Anita even bought Plymouth Plantation cookie cutters for me and, yes, we had Pilgrim cookies at Thanksgiving as my children preferred iced sugar cookies over pie—now that they're more grown up, some of them still do!

³/₄ C (1¹/₂ cubes) softened butter
³/₄ C sugar
1 large egg
1 tsp vanilla extract
2¹/₄ C flour
¹/₄ tsp salt
Water (optional)
Quick White Icing

Preheat oven to 350°F.

1. Cream butter in a large mixing bowl. (If you have a Kitchen Aid mixer, I have found that is the best tool in my kitchen, hands down! Mine has earned back every penny I spent on it!) Add sugar; beat until light and fluffy. Beat in egg and vanilla until well blended.

2. Mix flour and salt in a small bowl. Gradually add flour mixture to creamed butter and sugar until well blended and dough starts to pull away from the sides of the bowl. If the dough seems too dry, add water, 1 tsp at a time.

3. Roll dough into a ball on a lightly floured surface, cover with plastic wrap, and chill for 1 to 2 hours.

4. Preheat oven to 350°F. Roll half of chilled dough on lightly floured surface to a ¹/₈-inch thickness. (Using a cloth rolling-pin cover helps prevent the dough from sticking.) Cut the dough with cookie cutters dipped in flour. Repeat until all dough shapes are cut.

5. Place the dough shapes on buttered cookie sheets and bake for 10 to 12 minutes until cookies brown lightly around the edges.

6. While cookies are baking, prepare Quick White Icing.

7. Have your cooling rack and icing ready for when your cookies come out of the oven. Transfer the cookies carefully with a spatula from the cookie sheet and onto the cooling rack.

8. Ice cookies and let cool until hardened. (See tips that follow for decorating suggestions.)

TIPS: When frosting the cookies, I like to choose my base color and then have several different colors to pipe on after the original base color has cooled.

When decorating with chocolate pieces, wait until the cookies have cooled (I made jack-o-lantern faces with chocolate chips and broken chocolate pieces; they melted and ran everywhere because the cookies were still warm.)

Decorating with sprinkles is also a good idea. For these, sprinkle while the icing is still warm. Once the icing has cooled and hardened, the sprinkles will bounce off the cookie!

Icing your cookies when they are still warm creates a smooth, glazed look. After the iced cookies have cooled, you can pipe on your decorations and trim. I find placing the cookies in the refrigerator for 30 minutes is enough time to cool them.

QUICK WHITE ICING

Makes about ¾ C

From *Joy of Cooking*. (My old edition has a rubber band holding the falling pages and broken binding together. Should I replace it with a new edition? Naaah!)

2 C confectioner's sugar
¼ tsp salt
3 T softened butter
2 tsp vanilla
Cream (optional)

Sift together sugar and salt (this is mostly to remove any lumps in the sugar). Mix the butter and vanilla with the sugar mixture until smooth and somewhat thick. If the icing is too thin, add more confectioner's sugar; if it is too thick, add a little cream.

～

CLASSIC PIZZELLES

Makes 24–28 cookies

You can always halve the recipe for a smaller batch. But you might as well make the full batch, as these go FAST! You will need the special pizzelle iron to make this, which retails around $40 or more. Believe me, it'll be another great investment in your "comfort food" cooking gear!

6 eggs

1¹/₂ C sugar

1 C margarine, melted and cooled slightly

(Do not use more or substitute oil for the margarine;

butter can be substituted, but may burn.)

2 T vanilla (options: anise or lemon extract).

3¹/₂ C flour

4 tsp baking powder

1. Beat eggs until frothy. Add sugar to egg gradually and beat until smooth and thick.

2. Stir in cooled margarine and vanilla or other extract.

3. Sift flour with baking powder. Blend flour mixture into egg mixture until smooth.

4. Brush pizzelle iron with oil and heat until ready.

5. Batter will be sticky enough to be dropped by tablespoon onto each circle of the pizzelle iron (sometimes called pizzelle baker). The iron usually has at least two or more cookie templates. Bake until done—usually about 20 seconds. Pizzelles should be light brown.

6. Cover lightly with plastic wrap. Can be frozen, but these are best when fresh.

TIPS: Do not overcook. And do not put too much batter on the iron at a time. You will get the hang of how much is too much, as you don't want it to overflow the edges of the iron when pressed! You want a nice circle and not a lot of "overhang"! (You can trim any excess with a knife or kitchen shears.) Cookies should be thin and crispy when cooled.

For a festive look, dip half of each cooled cookie into melted dipping chocolate and cool on waxed paper.

Sprinkle each pizzelle with a dusting of powdered sugar for a snowy effect at holiday time.

7

DEALING WITH ANGER

Providing support to someone dealing with a life-threatening illness day after day can seem like a daunting, even an impossible task. Whether you are the immediate caregiver or a support person offering help, there are unanticipated situations and wrenching experiences to endure that most people aren't prepared to face. It is normal to feel angry. I felt angry because I had to watch my friend and later my son suffer day in and day out and was absolutely powerless to stop it. It is essential for you to find a healthy outlet for your anger. Let me share with you a few examples of how I worked through my anger during some especially difficult times.

My best friend, Becky, was diagnosed with stage 4 breast cancer in the fall of 1998. We were both young mothers of children ages three and five. I also had a nine-year-old child. Cancer was something I thought happened to older or less healthy people. When it did happen to Becky, I figured she was young, tough, and had a tremendous faith in God that would be more than enough to help her beat cancer. Yes, I had everything all figured out. Death was something I had never contemplated for my young, vital friend.

Difficult News

"Hey, Girl," a voice called out. Becky had been waiting for me on her darkened front steps as my car pulled up to her driveway.

"What are you doing out here?" I asked. Even though it wasn't raining, a cold nip was in the air; it was definitely autumn. Despite the chill, Becky wore neither a coat nor a sweater.

"I needed some space. I don't want the kids to hear what we're talking about," she explained, her voice tired. "I have breast cancer."

The words landed on me like a dead weight. I felt the air being sucked out of my lungs as I gasped and sat down to join her on the cold stone steps.

"The doctor found a lump a couple of weeks ago and I didn't want to worry anybody," she said. Becky paused and drew in a deep breath. "But after the biopsy report, doctors found out it was malignant. There's cancer in my lymph nodes and the tumor is about an inch in diameter. The doctor thinks with chemo and maybe surgery they can get rid of it," she explained numbly. I could barely see her face in the darkness. I was filled with fear and hardly knew what to say or how to react.

"Oh, my God, Becky. No way!" was all I could manage to utter as I slipped my arms around her in a loving embrace of friendship and solidarity. It was all I had to offer. Even though all I wanted to do was scream and cry out in pain and disbelief, I forced myself to say, "Becky, you will fight this. I mean you are one tough girl, with the greatest faith in God I know! You will get through this; we will get through this. You know, people do it all the time!"

I had run in the Race for the Cure, a National Breast Cancer fund-raiser, several times. I recalled all those survivors I had seen in their pink hats, women in their fifties and sixties, hugging each other and bravely walking together in the race. Afterward, scores of them waved triumphantly from the stands in the survivor's ceremony. I could picture Becky and me, the two of us standing together as the Survivor song played in the background. I envisioned Becky up there with a pink bandanna wrapped around her head and a radiant smile on her face. I would stand by her side.

Becky called out, "Hey, Kathy, did you hear me?" But I hadn't heard her. I had been carried away in my own dreams of Becky's future as a fully recovered cancer survivor.

As I came back to reality, I nodded and grinned defiantly, "Oh yeah, we'll kick some cancer ass!"

"I like that!" Becky's eyebrows shot up as she cried out. I saw some of her familiar wicked, mischievous humor return to her eyes. We both promised we

would pray hard and storm the gates of heaven with prayer requests and peti-
tions. After a few giggles and one really big hug, we went inside.

Months went by. Becky endured rounds of chemotherapy and surgeries
while support groups and friends rallied with every bit of help and affirmations
they had to help her live. Yet my hopes and dreams of a cure for Becky and for
her living to raise her family came crashing down one rainy cold Northwest evening as Becky confided her surrender.

I Just Can't Take It Anymore

"I just can't do it. I don't want to do this to my husband, to my children, to all
of you. But I can't help it!" Becky confessed as tears coursed down her cheeks. It
was early October 1998, and I was driving her home from the photo session our
care group had arranged that night. There was anger and frustration in her voice
as she said, "I go to chemo. I take all the meds the doctors tell me to, the blood
transfusions . . ." She sighed, exhaling deeply. "There's a stem-cell transplant and
a new miracle drug, too, but I have to get stronger for that. I'm trying
. . ." She wandered off as her breathing become slow and shallow. Becky struggled to catch her next breath. Her breast cancer was terminal and she was dying.

My mind raced, as I struggled to find the right words to say. Then I remembered something my mother used to say to me. I consoled her with the best
piece of advice I had to offer. "You know, Becky, when I was a little girl, my mom
used to tell me that all anyone can ask of you is that you do your very best.
You've done your best. That's all you can ask of yourself." Becky paused and
gazed over at me, her eyes open wide.

"Have you tried your best?" I asked, knowing full well she had.

"Yes, I have," she answered nodding her head up and down.

"Then that's all anybody, even God, can ask of you," I replied, hoping this
was the answer Becky would want to hear. I swallowed hard, knowing I could
add nothing further because I had no more voice, and my eyes were fogged over
with tears. Becky reached over and took my hand, and we drove in silence the
rest of the way.

Within, I didn't feel comforted at all. It wasn't fair. It couldn't be so
simple. *What about her husband, the kids, us?* I was grateful I had been able to
soothe Becky, yet my mother's words of comfort didn't console me. My emotions

and thoughts were jumbled and tangled like the computer wires and cords clumped behind my writing desk at home.

We pulled into her steep driveway, and I parked the car. As I opened the passenger door to try and guide her out, Becky's legs buckled beneath her. She hung between the edge of the car door and the seat.

"Get my husband! Quick!" Becky moaned, her eyes rolling into the back of her head.

"I can't. You might fall," I argued back, my heart racing.

Wild with fear, Becky called out, "Get David!"

Leaving her propped on the edge of the seat, praying she wouldn't slide out, I ran up the steps and banged on their front door.

"Becky's fallen and we need to get her inside!" I gasped and pointed over to the car.

David ran and nearly fell down the front stairs as we hurried to Becky. With each of us grabbing Becky beneath her arms, we hoisted her up, guided her up the driveway, and nearly lifted her inside.

Jill, her landlady, had heard the commotion and came to our aid at the front door. "Kathy, I can help David get Becky. It's late. You need to get home," I heard Jill say.

I didn't wait for more explanations. I had done all I could and knew it was time to leave. There was nothing more I could do, and I knew that Becky and her husband needed their privacy.

As I drove away, I heard myself protest to God, "She's done all she can do. Why her, God? Why can't You do more?" I choked out each word between gasps and sobs, waving my fists into the air. I had to pull my car to the side of the road, because I could barely see what was in front of me.

I smashed my fists down on top of my steering wheel in frustration and pain. "Where are You?" I demanded of God. "How could a loving God do this?" I hollered. "She has two beautiful children who need their mother." The faith that I had relied on so heavily, had drawn so much strength from in the months before, had deserted me.

The release of tears and anger gave me some relief. My friend was suffering and dying. She was also going to leave her husband and children far too soon. I was powerless to stop this tragedy. Who wouldn't feel anger at a time like this? Anger is a normal emotion when faced with such unbearable outcomes.

Releasing the emotion in a healthy way is important, both for your health and to fortify you so you can be present for whatever must be faced.

What follows is a story from when cancer hit our own family years after Becky's death. It describes how I broke down in anger and frustration from being my son's caregiver. Anger and frustration is inevitable for all those who face a life-threatening illness. Because it will flare up probably more than once, it's important to know that it's healthy to release the anger and to ask for help when you need it.

Cancer Sucks

On New Year's Day, both Paul and I were running fevers, with horrible body aches and screaming headaches to match. Because Conner's immune system was weakened by his chemotherapy treatments, we had to wear surgical masks to reduce the spread of germs any time we went near him. At this point in his treatment, Conner was on a naso-gastric feeding tube that needed to be changed every eight hours and an IV antibiotic pump that needed to be changed every four to six hours. The latter was a consequence of developing a central-line infection around Christmas. To deal with our exhaustion, Paul and I took turns changing Conner's feeding tube and administering the IV antibiotics.

Earlier that morning, I had collapsed on the floor of my walk-in closet in anger and exhaustion. I closed the door behind me and let loose by banging my fists on the floor, kicking some shoes, and screaming into a pile of laundry on the floor. Finally spent, I curled up into a ball and sobbed. I was too tired to continue my daily duties, and there was nobody left to take care of me. I felt horrible! But as Conner's caretaker, I had to rally and keep going, even when I didn't feel like it. I was tormented by thoughts of my extended family sitting on a warm, sunny beach in Mexico. If cancer hadn't struck our child, our family would be there, too.

At that moment, I thought I would give anything to be with them on that beach, instead of staying here to deal with this cancer nightmare. I watched Conner suffer day in and day out without cease, having to give up his former life and maybe never get it back again. Plus, I was unable to give my husband, Paul, or my other children, Jennifer and Patrick, the attention they deserved. I wanted our old life back. *Cancer just plain sucks!* I thought. Cancer is so isolating, cruel, and unfair. The holidays just exacerbated my sense of loss. I felt like life had moved on without us.

Looking back, I had a real and valid reaction to an excruciating time in our family's life. No matter how dramatic and selfish my reaction was, it was necessary to release those emotions. Put in an impossible situation, I rebelled, thinking: "I don't want to do this today!" I knew I had to be responsible. But for the moment, I took a break and let my emotions take center stage. I was not a saint or a martyr, just a mother whose child was dealt a lousy hand of cards. I tried to handle this difficult situation the best I could.

I also realized I needed to reach out to others and accept their many offers of help and not let my pride or need to be self-sufficient interfere with embracing the support we needed. I also realized that in my despair, it was time to find someone to talk to about my feelings, someone who understood and could help—a professional therapist, as well as a support group for parents of cancer patients.

Many of our friends and family told us how strong and amazing we were. Throughout, we did better some days than others. The important thing to know is that instead of rejecting or suppressing your anger, you deal with it in a healthy way. Here are a few suggestions that may help.

Letting It Out

- ♥ Go somewhere private: your car or a remote corner of a park, for example, and vent with a good yell or scream.
- ♥ Play some rock or heavy metal music and rock out to it. Or maybe play some spirited country-western music if that works best for you and stomp and holler.
- ♥ Work out hard, run, box, and or dance until you're exhausted. A physical release is very therapeutic.
- ♥ Bang some drums, hit a nail hard with a hammer, or chop some wood.
- ♥ Knead some bread dough. Pound it well to release your frustrations.
- ♥ Dig or hoe in the garden. Working in the dirt can be very cathartic.
- ♥ Power walk.
- ♥ Pray and try to hand it over to God.

8

You Are Not Alone

Caring for a loved one with a serious illness can lead to feelings of isolation and loneliness. You may feel that you are the only person or yours is the only family experiencing this magnitude of stress. I often felt that sense of separation among my friends. I yearned for the companionship of others who understood me, understood us through shared experiences. At such times of intense crisis, it seems like life goes on without you: in many ways it does. But, you are not alone. Others do care about you. And that life you see going on without you will be there to step back into when your situation resolves and you are ready.

There are always others like you who are experiencing similar challenges. It is a matter of discovering them and finding the support that comes from connecting with them. Other caregivers I met while caring for my friend Becky and later my son Conner helped me to cope in a way I desperately needed. Their experiences offered me new insight into my own and showed me I wasn't alone. I would like to share some experiences that show how making such connections fortified me in my struggle to help others deal with cancer.

Conner Reaches Out

It isn't only the caregivers who need to be reassured. When my son reached out to another cancer patient during treatment, it helped both boys feel better during a very difficult time in their treatments. And it drew Conner out of his shell just a bit.

I had just returned to the hospital, our second "home," after dropping off my older son, Patrick, at swim practice. I saw Diane, the mom I had met at our second chemotherapy hospital stay. She was standing outside the room with her son David, his IV stand and pole in hand. She took me aside and explained that David had had a very emotionally tough afternoon, becoming unusually agitated and anxious. I shook my head in sympathy, recognizing what it was like to hit bottom.

"But I have to tell you what really impressed me, Kathy, was how Conner reacted. He has been really sick. You can tell—he's been curled up in a ball under his covers all day. But when he heard David crying, he got up out of bed and started talking to him." Diane pushed her bangs away from her eyes and continued. "You know, he was distracting David, asking him questions about his favorite game, what book he was reading, reassuring him. I was so impressed and it really, really helped David calm down. Please thank him for me. You've got a great kid there. Thank you."

Her eyes were wet with emotion. I hugged her as we rocked back and forth in the hospital hallway, trying to hold one another up. It was encouraging to see that my son could transcend his own challenges to show compassion and empathy for others. Both Diane and I were moved by Conner's kindness in the darkest of times. This gave us a glimpse of hope that the boys wouldn't always be this sick.

Finding Other Cancer Parents

When my son underwent chemotherapy treatment, I discovered by chance I was not alone in his journey. I also learned to reach out to other parents and other families who shared parallel experiences.

Conner and I had checked into Children's Hospital for another long round of chemotherapy. He had had a rough first night and getting him comfortable was no easy feat. He slept in fitful two- to three-hour naps. At about 4 a.m., Conner grumbled about wanting something to eat. I arose from my armchair bed and shuffled down the hallway in a sleep-induced stupor in search of some sort of snack. That's when I ran into the mother of the boy who shared our room. Her careworn eyes and slept-in clothing resembled those of many of the parents who frequented the hallways of the oncology unit night and day. I raised my head in greeting, and our eyes met.

"Hi, my name is Kathy." I smiled weakly and was met with a warm, yet tired smile and eyes that didn't quickly dart away in avoidance or look cast down. On previous clinic and our last hospital visits, I had encountered brief smiles and turned-away heads and eyes, which signaled personal boundaries were being set; too much pain lived here, and no conversation would be shared. My heart leapt at the chance to connect with another cancer parent.

"Hi. My name is Diane. My son's name is David," she offered.

I nodded in acknowledgment. "My son is Conner. He's fourteen and is here with Ewing's Sarcoma."

"David is, too. He's twelve. Where is Conner's tumor?" Diane asked incredulously.

Neither of us could believe we had met another with the same cancer at the same time, in the same room. *What were the odds of finding another Ewing's Sarcoma patient, a rare form of cancer, and so close in age to Conner?* I wondered.

"In his scapula. And David?" I asked, feeling an immediate kinship with this woman.

"His jaw."

My mouth fell open. I had never heard of such an unusual location, as it usually develops in the pelvis or large bones. The skull or jaw was especially rare.

"Yeah, I know," shrugged Diane as she reached into the common refrigerator of the parent's room and pulled out a small Tupperware bowl. "They found it during a routine dental visit. He had been having some jaw pain."

"What's that?" I pointed to the homemade food she was stirring with a spoon.

"This? Leftover dinner. David won't touch anything from the hospital. We live just a few miles from here, so I bring everything from home. Don't worry, you'll get used to it." She smiled as she continued preparing a small meal for David.

"We can bring your own food?" I asked.

"Yup, most people do. The kids get really sick and get weird cravings and want stuff at different times and you just have to be ready," she said. "But it's really just for extra taste since David's feeding tube takes care of all of all his basic nutrition."

"Really?" I was curious. I dreaded the NG tube, but I felt it would be our fate sooner rather than later.

"Oh, yeah, it has made our life so much easier. I don't have to worry about David's nutrition or calorie counts. His weight gain has been good—one less thing to worry about." Diane smiled as good-naturedly as she could, given the situation in which we both found ourselves. "Well, I've got to get back," she motioned, heading out the door. "I'll see ya," Diane called out as she waved and disappeared down the hall.

As I walked back to our room, I tried to cheer myself with thoughts of my good fortune in meeting someone who was dealing with the same diagnosis as Conner. It was bittersweet to be thankful both boys were battling the same cancer. Grueling as chemotherapy was for my son, and for me as his mother and caregiver while I watched the toll it took on him, knowing there was someone else out there who was journeying along a similar path offered a ray of light. Diane and David were several months ahead of us in treatment and they were still persevering. Drawing from their example, so could we.

Over time, I continued to reach out to other moms whose children had cancer. The hospital social worker gave me the name of a mom named Barb, whose son Nick had finished chemotherapy treatment for Ewing's Sarcoma two years earlier. I decided to call her a few weeks before Conner's surgery was scheduled.

As I picked up the phone, my hands shook slightly. I didn't know the woman I was calling or how I'd be received by her.

"Is Barb Schaeffer there?" I asked nervously.

"Speaking. Who is this?" I heard a cheerful voice on the other end of the phone.

"Hi, Barb, this is Kathy Opie. I was given your phone number by Wendy, the social worker at Children's Hospital. My son has Ewing's Sarcoma and she told me you would be willing to talk about it with me," I explained, relieved that the woman sounded so eager to speak with me. "Your son also had Ewing's Sarcoma?"

"Oh yes, sure, Kathy. I would love to talk to you." I could feel her smile come across the phone. The tension I felt earlier melted away like spring snow as we had a pleasant conversation that flowed easily. Barb shared how her son Nick had had Ewing's in his pelvis and was now two years cancer free. He also endured chemotherapy and radiation and had worn a body cast for six weeks after his surgery.

"I can come down tomorrow to Children's and meet you for coffee," offered Barb. I jumped at the chance. I said I couldn't wait to meet her and was pleased that she could come to the hospital on such short notice.

The next day, I searched the hospital coffee shop, not knowing what Barb looked like and wondering where she might be sitting. I then spotted a kindly looking woman in a denim skirt and comfortable warm sweater, with short brown hair and soft brown eyes. She was holding a gift bag stuffed with lime green and yellow tissue paper. The woman seemed comfortable in her surroundings and with herself, as if she had been here before. Immediately, I knew it was Barb.

"Kathy?" she asked as I approached the table.

"Hi, Barb!" I smiled and sat down.

Barb pushed the gift bag toward me. "These are for you."

"Oh, thank you!" I cried and noticed she had given me a thoughtful gift of travel-sized shower gel, lotion, and shampoo from the Bath and Body Shop, along with some hard candies for Conner. These gifts were appropriately given from someone who had been in our shoes before. I was drawn to Barb's calm presence and strength. Hers was a gentle strength, earned by surviving something horrific. Through it, she had gained the ability to rise above day-to-day trivialities to see what really matters. She was far enough removed from the situation to not still be in the reactive crisis mode I was. I was drawn to her like a moth to a flame. She reassured me that her son responded much the same way as Conner did to his treatments: quiet, humble, and just wanting to be left alone, without fuss or drama. She also reminded me how well Conner was responding to chemotherapy. He'd only needed one blood transfusion, when usually multiple ones were required.

After our talk, I felt much better. Barb assured me I could call her anytime. I promised her I would, and I often did.

Finding Barb was a blessing. She offered calm assurance from having survived a similar illness at a time when I was in the midst of the storm and couldn't see my way out. Calling on her when I felt hopeless and lost was so helpful and gave me the determination to stay positive on days when it was very difficult to do so.

The CaringBridge

During our long days of confinement at home due to Conner's weakened immune system and our extended hospital stays, the CaringBridge website offered us a way to stay connected to our larger community through social media. I was able to blog about what had transpired on a given day either from my home computer or a computer terminal provided for us at the hospital. I could also check messages throughout the day and correspond as desired. It was an ideal way to reduce the loneliness and isolation and ease the burden of sending out multiple messages during stressful times.

As well, friends and family sent encouraging comments or left uplifting messages at any time of the day or night. These were invaluable, especially during Conner's tension-filled surgery or when he was very sick. In addition to tending your own flow of messages, you can visit the CaringBridge sites to get updates on others and track their journeys.

Saying Goodbye to a Friend

While she was hospitalized during the later stages of her illness, I came each day to spend time with Becky. I knew her end was near, but one never really knows exactly how close. This particular day, a large group of friends, her husband, children, and extended family had convened on the oncology floor. I had met some in the gift shop, in the cafeteria, and along the hallways. We had been arriving in shifts to visit Becky.

I dropped in to her hospital room during one of my turns and saw that her children had just finished visiting their mother. It was to be their last visit. My friend Becky was saying goodbye to them for the last time. She held out her arms to them. In an instant, I realized the significance of this final parting and felt as if an invisible fist had knocked the wind out of me.

Jake walked over to hug his mother, but she was in so much pain that she could only manage a light kiss and a stroking of his arm and hair. She wanted so badly to hold him, to touch him one more time. She moaned in both physical and emotional pain. Next was Annelisa's turn. Annelisa wanted to jump up on the bed and cuddle with her mommy. What six-year-old wouldn't? Each time she attempted it, Becky would cry out and Annelisa's face would crumble in fear and grief. She didn't understand; she just wanted her mommy.

I stepped to the edge of the bed. "Becky what can I do?" I pleaded.

"I can't hold her. It hurts, it hurts," Becky moaned.

"What if I hold her above you? You could hug her, but her weight wouldn't be on you? Can I give that a try?" I asked gingerly. Annelisa was not small, but I managed to lift her for a brief moment over her mother.

"Now, Annelisa, you can give your mommy a hug and kiss from up here without hurting her sore muscles and bones, okay, Honey?" I tried to explain.

"I love you, Baby, I love you," Becky cried and stroked her daughter's cheek, kissing her over and over.

"I love you, too, Mommy. I love you, I love you," Annelisa said, her big brown eyes brimming with tears and love. My arms began to shake and quiver from the strain of holding Annelisa.

"Okay, Honey, I have to put you down now," I croaked as tears ran down my cheeks. Annelisa took one last sorrowful look at her mom and ran across the room to Jill, the family's landlady and now caregiver.

Becky's face was red, splotchy, and streaked with tears. "Now you kids be good and behave, you hear," she cried out weakly across the room.

"Of course they will, Becky. That's the way you raised them. They're always good and well-behaved." Jill beamed brightly, her eyes brimming with tears.

"You be good," Becky warned once more, weakly, shaking her finger at them. I knew it was her last attempt at mothering, her last turn at taking care of her children and helping bring them up, at any participation or control. I couldn't contain the flood of emotions welling up inside me. I had to leave the room. I turned to wave a quick goodbye to the family before nearly running down the hall to find the nearest restroom for privacy.

Afterward, I had a quiet dinner in the hospital cafeteria. The food was nourishing and heavy, and I was grateful for the comfort food and for a small reprieve from the fifth floor. Luckily, I had tucked a book inside my purse and quickly lost myself in its pages after finishing my meal. I couldn't shake off the emotions I felt, knowing that I had just held a child for her mother to say goodbye to her, probably for the very last time. I didn't want to have to do that, could have never imagined myself offering to do such a thing, but there I was doing the unthinkable. Becky's pastor and his wife were upstairs when I returned to her room after dinner. I was happy to see them as I entered the room because they brought such a sense of peace and prayer with them.

"Hello, Kathy," I heard Pastor Marcus and his wife, Meko, say in unison.

"Hi. It's so good to see you, both of you," I smiled gratefully. "Becky is having a hard day. I didn't notice the catheter and oxygen here the other day," I reported, hoping for some encouragement from the pastor and his wife.

More visitors came in and out of Becky's room, some from her church and some from her core group of friends. I sat outside with Joan, the owner of the fish-and-chip house where Becky had worked until just recently. Joan had just been through a divorce, and the pain of it was still fresh. We talked about pain. Whether caused by grief over Becky, the loss of a husband or a child, or difficult childhood issues—pain is pain.

Jan, whom I had just met from our group photograph with Becky, came over and clapped me on the shoulders. "Hey, Honey, how are ya holding up?"

"I've been better," I scoffed and gave her a tired smile.

"I hear you on that one. What are you ladies jawin' about now?" she kidded and slid into one of the chairs lining the hallway.

"There is something worse than death," I confessed to Jan and Joan as the terrible, yet comforting realization flooded over me.

"Oh really?" Joan looked at me, a puzzled, worried look crossing her face.

"This indefinite suffering, having to say a final goodbye to your children, being in so much pain you can barely breathe or hold up your head anymore," I said bitterly.

We sat in silence for a few moments. I felt I had aged many years in the last few days. Then I shared my faith-based assurances. "I know there are angels surrounding Becky now, I can just *feel* their presence. That's the reward, that's the gift, not lingering here in agony."

"I know what you mean," Joan finally responded and patted me on the knee.

"Amen, Sister!" Jan agreed and got up to check in on Becky.

I was surprised at how close I felt to all of the women who had come to visit Becky. Some sat by the top of her bed, mopping her brow with a cool compress. Others arranged her many vases of flowers, while Meko organized the baked goods and meals people had brought for the family.

After we had visited with Becky, people made their way out to the night-darkened hospital parking lot. I awaited my ride. When my husband and I drove off, the women waved warmly. I could see their careworn, tired faces. They had jobs to go to the next day and lives of their own waiting for them at home.

Although I thought the whole world should stand still and mourn for Becky, I realized that life does go on, even if you aren't ready for it to do so. When we are suffering, it can feel like we are moving underwater in slow motion. We go through the paces of day-to-day life and try somehow to get through each day, one day at a time, one hour at a time if we have to.

By coming together at the hospital in our common goal of helping our dear friend Becky, we discovered we could find comfort and solace in our shared love and care of her. We formed a community with its roots in our shared grief, our sorrow, and our experiences together. We learned that we were united and together, not alone.

You Are Not Alone

There are many ways to ease the sense of isolation and loneliness that is inherent in caretaking a loved one with a life-threatening illness. The most powerful is to reach out and discover you are not alone in your journey, that there are others out there like you who are struggling and coping each day with a similar disease or illness. It will help you maintain the strength you need to continue meeting your responsibilities.

I have offered a few stories of how I reached out or even stumbled upon opportunities to bond and connect with others in my community who were experiencing similar hardships. Making these connections gave me a sense of comradery and support. When weathering the demands of caregiving and the mental, physical, and emotional toll it brings, finding others with whom to share your journey is critical. Doing so refuels and refreshes the caregiver, bringing hope during a time when you need it most.

- ♥ Listen alertly while in clinic, or in a support group, or in your hospital room. You may learn someone has a very similar situation to yours, and you can follow up with him or her.

- ♥ Be proactive. While in clinic or at the hospital, if you feel able and with sensitivity, ask other caregivers for what illness or disease their loved ones are being treated. If they respond positively, you have an opportunity to pursue a mutually beneficial connection, one that will reduce your feelings of isolation. As well, you may learn valuable lessons about how to cope with your loved one's disease.

♥ Ask your hospital social worker for the names of people who are willing to talk to you about their experience with treatment.

♥ Ask your care provider or hospital social worker for the location of the hospital resource center where you might find reading material, visual aids, and perhaps a directory of support groups related to your patient's disease or illness. Writing or emailing these groups for information and support is beneficial.

9

TAKING CARE OF THE CAREGIVER

How do you find the time to take care of yourself when you are taking care of a loved one who is struggling to survive? Despite my husband and friend's pleas to take a break, I hardly left my son's bedside for the first several months of his illness. There were days when I couldn't even find time to shower. I lived in my sweatsuit so I could awake within seconds from either a 2 p.m. catnap or a 2 a.m. emergency wake-up call. I was also in too much shock to think of anything other than my son and his care. I simply was not a priority.

Yet, the signs of my stress and fatigue were clear to others. I snapped at my family, couldn't sleep through the night, and cried frequently. Caregiver burnout, a common phenomenon, can lead to multiple negative health effects, including decreased immune function, sleep disturbance, depression, grief, exhaustion, and anxiety. I realized that I couldn't remain a compassionate or effective caregiver if I became depleted. After my son's first central-line infection, his nurse told me I looked utterly exhausted. I finally realized I needed to take some time out to recharge.

Activities that Give Relief

Stepping out of the intensity of the caregiving environment by either walking or jogging outdoors for a few minutes provided me a reprieve and time to collect my thoughts and refocus. Before my son became ill, I was a runner. I found comfort in doing a familiar activity. I also knew it was a healthy activity and a good physical outlet for my pent-up emotions and frustrations—which were greater than usual. When I couldn't leave Conner, I engaged in quieter, sedentary activities that offered me some respite. Mine were simple activities, such as reading a magazine or a daily devotion, writing a quick journal entry, playing handheld Yahtzee, doing a word search, Sudoku, or crocheting. These activities weren't too mentally or emotionally demanding, and they distracted me from the stress I felt.

To free me for some necessary break times, my friends would volunteer time on the Caregiver Calendar for caregiver breaks in two-hour increments twice a week. Some days, I used the time to run errands, go for a jog, or spend time with my husband. Other days, I would meet a friend for coffee, get a massage, or take a long, relaxing walk. Whether I took these breaks depended on the state of Conner's health; if he was well enough for me to leave him with someone else, I had many things to do that helped me recharge.

The Red Afghan

During the long months of caretaking my son Conner, I started crocheting a red afghan. Red is Conner's favorite color, and I chose to keep things simple by using a single color, stitch, and pattern so I could put down and later pick up my project easily. Keeping my hands busy and focusing on the stitches and patterns soothed me as those red circles and loops of yarn tumbled from my crochet hook. I felt productive and useful. The afghan project was also a wonderful ice-breaker for the rounds of hospital personnel who came in and out of our room. The bright red blanket growing on my lap was hard to miss.

"Hey, that looked like a scarf last time you were here: now look at you go," one bright-eyed young nurse commented as she replaced Conner's IV.

"Yeah, I'm hoping to make an afghan or even a bedspread for Conner. We'll see how far I get," I commented as I continued working the yarn and crochet hook.

"Keep up the good work. You know, they have knitting groups that meet upstairs every week. You should check them out," she added and smiled encouragingly. I nodded, wondering if I would have the chance to leave my son's side. It was great to know that others had discovered the soothing comfort of yarn work.

My stress level could be measured by the many rows I had crocheted by the end of a hospital stay.

The afghan, which was finished a few months after Conner's last chemotherapy treatment, helped me imagine a time and place where there would be no more cancer. Today, that red afghan has now gone off to college with Conner.

Hitting the Burke-Gilman Trail

My lifesaver during my son's illness was jogging, especially with a friend. While Conner was receiving inpatient chemotherapy, my friend Debbie often came from her home south of Seattle Children's Hospital. She not only provided opportunities for me to leave the hospital for a time and go for a run, but gave essential companionship and support to me during a time when I felt emotionally depleted. Debbie was a seasoned marathon runner. She advised me that running didn't have to be about flogging oneself to go harder and faster. She taught me that as I ran, I could relax and feel my breathing to get in tune with my body. Before her wise counsel, I had been sneaking out of the hospital before Conner awoke in the mornings, returning exhausted, the runs less than satisfying. Looking back, I realized Debbie's relaxing breathing technique wasn't only useful for running, but could be applied in many areas in my life to help me de-stress.

"Hey, you look good," Debbie smiled at Conner as she entered the dimly lit oncology room, recognizing the soft brown and blue striped beanie Conner wore that she'd given him on her last visit. He hadn't removed it from his head since.

"Yup, I like it," Conner smiled shyly as he rolled his eyes upward. He gave us both a quick nod of acknowledgment. Conner, spotting Debbie's gym bag, asked if we were going running.

"That's right. I was hoping to take your mom for a run, if that's okay with you. We won't be gone very long," Debbie reassured, glancing over at her bag.

"You guys go. Mom needs a break. I'll be fine," Conner assured us. We made sure Conner was comfortable, told his nurse where I was going and that I had my cell phone with me and would be back in one hour.

"Why don't you listen to those books on tape your teacher assigned to you," I suggested, knowing he was better off tuned into his books on tape than to a television.

"Okay, okay," Conner protested as I kissed his head.

It was a warm spring day as Debbie and I began our run along Seattle's Burke-Gilman Trail near the hospital. A soft breeze brushed against our limbs as we started into our stride. We entered the lush, forested trails.

"Conner is doing really well," Debbie offered, as we continued running. I was pleased to hear her positive perspective and instantly began to feel better.

"Now let's work on your running," she continued. "I want you to count your breathing and really listen as the breath passes into and out of your body. If you're panting or gulping for breath, you're pushing your body too hard."

We both laughed as I said I felt like a beached fish gulping for air. I couldn't remember the last time I had laughed out loud and it felt good. We continued our run under the canopy of green trees. Light filtered down through the leaves and created lacy patterns upon the ground beneath. The pebble-strewn path was dotted with wildflowers on the sides, and the air was scented with moist earth and foliage. I was grateful to be in the moment with my friend and out in nature.

But soon thoughts of my reality set in and, as we slowed to a walk, I shared my heart. "I'm always waiting for the other shoe to drop—you know, what if the cancer comes back? What if the chemotherapy doesn't work and he gets sick again or takes a turn for the worse and there are complications like an infection?" I asked.

"I know you're scared, and that's so natural with all you've been through. But look how far you all have come. Conner is one tough kid and you guys are one tough family." There was steely resolution in Debbie's voice. "Don't let the cancer win!" she added, and I knew she was talking not only about the physical disease, but also the emotional and mental toll it takes.

Friends are a crucial lifeline during this hospital time. They can lend a calm and perspective that you may not have while you are in the midst of these trying, worrisome days. Call on them for encouragement and support. In addition to availing myself of the scheduled care-calendar time my friends had signed up for, I also tried to accept spontaneous offers from family and friends to help when Conner wasn't too sick to be left without us or wasn't in the hospital. I found that Paul and I needed time together as a couple. Caregiving can be exception-ally demanding on a marriage. As a caregiver, your relationship with your spouse or significant other may suffer. Yet there is encouraging research that shows if you share the responsibilities of caregiving, you can actually bond more and grow stronger as a couple.

Cozy Table for Two

Marriages need to be nurtured, even during a life-threatening illness. Our college-age daughter realized this and offered to stay home with Conner one evening while she was home during Christmas break. Paul and I desperately needed a date night, but were reluctant to leave Conner. At our daughter's insistence, we finally agreed.

As we headed out, the roads grew icy, and a menacing wind threatened a storm. Paul and I joked that we wouldn't let one more thing get in the way of our precious date night. We'd named this our "Stalingrad Christmas," as it didn't feel much like a Christmas at all.

After we arrived at the restaurant, we stomped our shoes to shake off the snow and then entered the warm foyer. There we were welcomed to sit before the blazing fire that roared in the stone fireplace. As we ordered our drinks and read the menu amidst the cacophony of merry holiday patrons and background Christmas music, we tried our best not to feel like aliens just dropped to Earth from another planet. It was a struggle to be normal after having spent the last three months in and out of the hospital and in near-isolation with our son. We made it a point not to complain or talk about CBCs (blood counts) or to engage in hospital speak on our special night.

"What?" I joked self-consciously as Paul tried to read my face in the dimly lit room.

"You were about to say something?" Paul asked. I found it difficult to manufacture conversation, but I kept trying for the sake of our date night.

"I was going to say that Conner would have loved a big juicy steak from here if he had his appetite," I mused. "But I promised we'd just focus on us. So how are you? If this wasn't 2009, what would you like to be doing for Christmas this year?" I feigned a smile.

"Oh, that's easy!" Paul answered. "We would be skiing or snowboarding. This weather is great for that, don't you think? Do you remember last year?" His voice trailed off.

Before the giant fireplace Paul raised his glass and toasted, "Here's to us, to Conner, to kicking cancer's ass, and to not being here next year! We'll be going skiing. The kids can ski and you and I can spend the day alone in the cabin together." When he winked at me, his turquoise blue eyes twinkled mischievously.

"Sounds good," I answered, blushing, an ember beginning to glow deep inside of me. I was grateful to realize that romance still burned in our marriage.

"We can continue this date back at home," Paul teased and reached for my hand across the table.

Sharing the Care

Paul and I had a special term for our shared caregiving that we called "tag team." From the beginning of Conner's treatment, we decided that we'd always make sure that one of us was with our two boys at all times, and we would check in regularly with our daughter who was away at college. Our sixteen-year-old son, Patrick, would always have a parent with him at home and at either school or sporting events. We hoped this would help our sons not feel abandoned by either parent during Conner's treatment. But it did make spending time together as a couple more challenging.

Paul would bring his laptop to the hospital when it was his turn to attend to Conner. Whenever he could concentrate, Paul would answer work-related email and, if he was able to step away for a few minutes, he would take work calls in a public area. If not, he played laptop video games or watched movies.

When Conner was feeling well, he and Paul would play a dual-player video game. They seemed to enjoy this time together. Paul rarely felt the need to leave the hospital room when he stayed with Conner. He mentioned that maintaining his forty-hour-a-week job and spending time with supportive coworkers gave him the mental and physical break needed from attending to Conner.

Yet this relentless work schedule and the forty-five-mile round-trip commute to the hospital, plus the stress of seeing things a parent shouldn't see a child endure, took its toll on our relationship. Research shows that many caregivers resort to self-medication as a way of coping. We were no exception: we found ourselves drinking far more often than we normally would have.

This is why it's important to seek counseling for support. Many people who have experienced this journey, including Paul and I, have found it crucial to go to couples counseling to repair the damage done to their marriage. Be sure to seek the help you need, both during and after treatment.

The Rejuvenating Benefits of Massage

I read on the message board outside the hospital family center that fifteen-minute free massages were being given to parents. I signed up for an appointment on the spot. Slipping away for just those few minutes to feel the skilled hands of the hospital massage therapist, I found the knots and tension that had formed in my shoulders over the last weeks melted beneath her experienced touch. As Ursula Popp, licensed sacro-cranial massage therapist explains, it feels so good to have "someone paying attention to you, versus you paying attention to someone else. So often you are only paying attention to the patient, and during massage therapy you are the center of attention," she explains.

Many hospital family centers have massage therapists who donate their time to give caregivers a free massage. It is also healing to schedule an extended massage every so often to relieve your muscle fatigue and tension. As you receive total attention and care from the massage therapist, you will feel rejuvenated.

How Should I Recharge?

I discovered that by accepting help from friends and family, I was able to schedule some much-needed breaks for myself. I found certain activities to be more life-giving and refreshing than others. You may need fewer or more breaks than others. You also may react to stress differently or have diverse support systems. Each situation is unique. It is important not to compare yourself to other caregivers in this regard. Just remember to take care of yourself so you can provide the best support for your loved one, as well as continue to lead a functional life within your family and community.

As I became more aware of the free community services or hospital/volunteer activities available, I discovered more options for support and fun. This is especially important when finances are strained during times of extended illness.

Here are ideas for activities that you might find helpful.

～ *Find or Create a Group that Inspires or Supports You: I reached out to fellow cancer moms and helped to create a parent support group.*

～ *Engage in Physical Activities:*

♥ Run on local trails or in an indoor gym, either alone, with your partner, or with a good friend.

♥ Walk outside to get a break from the caregiving setting when you have the opportunity. If he or she is well enough, you can also have your loved one join you by either walking or being pushed in a wheelchair.

♥ Go for a swim in a local pool or, if the weather permits, at a beach.

♥ Take a yoga class. There are also videos you can download online and practice yoga at your own pace and skill level in a home setting.

♥ Go for a hike near your home or the hospital as time and resources permit.

♥ Take a bike ride, participate in a spin class, or use a stationary bike for exercise.

♥ Go kayaking or canoeing and get out into nature.

♥ Work out at a local gym.

~ *Plan Social Time:*

♥ Meet a friend for coffee or a meal.

♥ Attend a sporting event.

♥ Go to see a movie, especially a funny one. Often laughter is good medicine and gives you a necessary break from thinking about your problems.

~ *Schedule Time for Personal Attention:*

♥ Get a soothing and healing massage to relieve tension in your mind and body.

♥ Take care of yourself and schedule a hair appointment.

♥ Go for a spa treatment and/or get your nails done with a friend or by yourself.

~ *Have Plenty of Creative/Quiet Activities:*

♥ Enjoy handcrafts such as embroidery or needlepoint. Crocheting or knitting handwork is also soothing and can take your mind off of worrisome problems.

♥ Draw or paint to express your feelings.

♥ Play crossword puzzles or Sudoku to keep your mind busy.

♥ Enjoy some light reading, something you can easily pick up or put down. I found short stories or magazine articles worked best for me.

♥ Enjoy a video game with a friend or group of friends.

♥ Journal about your feelings or go online and join a chat group with other caregivers who share similar issues.

10

GET OUT THERE!

Another way for the caregiver to feel a sense of empowerment during a difficult time is to get out there and join others in supporting a shared cause. Charities and local events that champion your loved one's illness can provide a great outlet and connect you with people who share a similar passion for getting the one you are caring for well and/or raising funds to research a cure. When my husband and I became involved in events that transcended us and Conner's illness, we found a sense of hope and promise for tomorrow. Even if your loved one's prognosis for recovery is marginal, taking part in the cause for a cure can leave a lasting legacy and you could be a part of that.

The following story describes a time when our friend Becky was in very late-stage breast cancer. I took some time out from caregiving and worrying about her to participate with my husband in the Race for the Cure.

Running In the Race for the Cure

Late in her cancer treatment, I told Becky I was dedicating my run to her in the Race for the Cure. She was very proud of me and told me she wanted to be there.

"You can push me in the wheelchair. I can cheer you on!" Becky teased, her tired eyes shining with a glimmer of pleasure. A terminal disease such as Becky's can make a caregiver feel quite powerless to affect the patient's recovery or ease her suffering. I was happy that day to bring some good news. But her desire to observe the race firsthand wasn't meant to be. By race day, Becky was far too sick to leave the confines of the hospital.

"I will bring you souvenirs—my race number and a race T-shirt. I can even get you a poster for your room and any other Race for the Cure goodies I can find," I promised Becky on our last visit before the race. I held her dry, thin hand in my own. She nodded carefully. "You see, Paul and I will be right over there." I pointed to the University of Washington Husky Stadium and tried to swipe at a stubborn tear escaping down my cheek. My voice faltered and I promised, "We will be out there running for you."

Becky's other hand reached out for me as I heard her shift position in her bed with some effort. "I am okay. I am so proud of you. Now go run and come back to me," she said with measured words.

Her breathing was becoming labored; the cancer had spread to her lungs. When you cannot alleviate your loved one's symptoms, you are often left with unresolved and bitter feelings. I found it helpful to process these feelings through physical exertion, especially through the rhythmic breathing of running.

The day for the Race for the Cure came early, as Paul and I packed our water bottles, post-race jackets, and snacks. The kids stayed at a friend's house for the night. I was excited. I would make Becky proud! I had no pre-race jitters, because, in my mind, this race was already dedicated and won. My spirit glowed the whole drive into Seattle, and my heart raced with the anticipation of the crowds and the adrenalin rush and emotion that came with such a big, highly advertised race.

But when I saw the hospital nearby, my heart sank. Becky was up there, same cancer. This day was no different for her than any other day. There would be no bright sunshine, no crowds cheering—just cancer, the white walls of the hospital, the nurses, and the IV chemo drip.

"Are you alright?" Paul asked.

"Yeah, I'm sorry, I can't help thinking about her. I just wish she could be here that's all." Becky was the reason I was running, and she wasn't here. I missed her terribly. I felt so powerless. It just wasn't fair.

"She's with you here. Remember the promise you made?" Paul pointed at my heart and smiled that big, bright smile that always lit up my heart. "Just run."

"You're right, let's go," I said. Paul always knew just the right thing to say.

After we pulled into a parking spot, we gathered our racing gear. Husky Stadium loomed large, dwarfing us with its towering overhangs and endless steps. The football field looked like a postage stamp in the middle of everything. I couldn't help running down the steps toward the infield in anticipation. I was going to gather up every race token, free gift, and item offered.

"Hold on, wait for me!" I heard Paul call from behind me.

"Come on, we want to be first for all the goodies," I called back. We registered at the main table and were handed our bag full of coupons, a race number and, most importantly, our Race for the Cure T-shirts. We couldn't claim we ran the race without sporting our very cool long-sleeved T-shirts.

We continued along the rows of booths. I felt like a little kid at Halloween, going from booth to booth with my trick-or-treat bag. I collected pencils, breast cancer pins, pads of paper, water bottles, wrist guards, key chains, pens, coupons, and snack samples—one for each of us. We came to a bandanna booth, where a bald woman sported a cute pink headwrap covered with the iconic folded pink ribbons. She smiled, but her eyes looked tired. I was immediately drawn to her.

"These are really wonderful," I exclaimed as I fingered the soft fabric of a few of the samples strewn on the table.

"Yes and they are very comfortable." The woman pointed to several other styles.

"My friend has quite a few, but I like this style," I remarked in appreciation.

"Your friend has breast cancer?" the woman asked, now interested.

"Yes, I'm running for her today. She's over there." I pointed to the University Hospital across the street. "I want to get things from the race and decorate her room with it, you know, as if she were actually here. She wanted to be, but the doctor said her blood counts were too low. She'd be here if she could." I couldn't stop talking.

Paul reached over and took my hand. "It's okay, Kathy."

"It's great you're doing this for her. I bet she really appreciates it." The woman grinned, but her eyes said more.

I felt my stomach drop as I tried to read those eyes for answers and found none.

"Good luck," she said. "Here's a bandanna for your friend."

"Thank you." I smiled and hurried away, not wanting to start crying. I focused on finding a race poster to complete Becky's ensemble.

"Hey, Kathy, we better get to the starting line. It's getting close to race time," Paul warned. We could hear the crowds getting hyped up for the start of the race and people beginning to get out of their warm-up gear and pare down to just T-shirts and race shorts.

Soon it was time for the race lineup. We were supposed to line up under our estimated mile-time placard. Paul edged toward the seven-minute-mile sign.

"You've got to be kidding me, right?" I scoffed. "There's no way I'm going that fast."

"You're going to surprise yourself. Besides, you don't want to be stuck in the back trying not to be trampled and trying to pass everyone as they dodge all around," he explained.

"Okay, I guess today anything is possible," I reluctantly agreed. That's when I saw some very tall, extremely muscular and impeccably dressed runners come out of the woods from behind the stands. "That's odd," I said to Paul. "Who are those guys?" I pointed to the huge men scattering themselves throughout the crowd.

"Secret Service Agents," Paul offered. "Didn't you hear? Al Gore is running with us today."

"Too cool!" I exclaimed. "Wait until I tell Becky! She's going to be so excited. This is her race you know?"

"I know, I know." Paul smiled and kissed me on the cheek.

"Good morning, runners! Isn't it a beautiful morning in Seattle?" the loud-speakers blared and teased, since we all knew it was a typical damp Seattle day. This was the start of our pre-race pep talk. "Are you psyched to run today?" We all cheered in response. "Do you want to beat breast cancer once and for all?" To which we answered with a deafening shout that shook and rattled my entire body!

I looked around at all the people here today. I saw T-shirts with people's pictures printed on them: these were images of both survivors and of those who had succumbed to breast cancer. I turned away from those shirts.

In anticipation of the race's start, I felt adrenalin rush through my body, leg muscles tensed, feet tingling, my arms pumped and ready to go. Paul and I were sandwiched between layers of people. We could hear the low rumble of feet jogging in place, the murmur of pre-race talk—*Hey, good luck. This your first race? First time doing the Race for the Cure?*—and the rustle of Gortex, nylon, and mesh running gear.

Suddenly, the announcer called, "Runners, the countdown is about to begin. All together . . . ten, nine, eight . . . " We all shouted out each number with growing anticipation, the volume increasing with every number. It was like New Year's Eve, but at the count of one you were to take off like a shot, with a wave of people surrounding you.

"Are you ready?" I asked Paul.

"Better question is are you?" he teased.

"Never more ready. Let's get this party started," I taunted.

It was a drizzly, gray Seattle September morning. The last green leaves of summer dangled from the branches. I admired their tenacity. We would need a lot of that today. Soon, Paul and I jogged past the starting gate. That was as fast as we could go, hemmed in as we were on all four sides. We dodged in and out around runners, jockeying for a better position. I kept sprinting ahead to pass a group of runners. Before long, the speed felt nice, the air burned my lungs, and my muscles stung. But it began to feel surprisingly . . . good.

"What are you doing, Kathy?" Paul asked in exasperation after we passed the first timing area.

"I'm trying to get ahead of this pack," I called back, breathing hard between words.

"Do you know we're doing a seven-and-a-half-minute mile pace?" Paul asked.

"Really?" I panted as I strode forward. I had a great stride going and didn't want anything to break it. I felt like I was caught up in a swift strong current, and I never wanted it to end.

"Are you sure you want to keep this up?" Paul yelled toward me, his face etched with concern.

"Yep," I breathed through my big grin and teased Paul with my eyes to come and catch me. This was going to be fun. We sailed past Vice President Gore. He looked older and balder than he did on television. Although I wondered if he was here for more than a political plug, I gave him credit for being out here on a rainy, gray morning to run for a worthy cause.

I kept sprinting ahead to pass a group of runners. Despite the air that burned my lungs and the sting in my calf muscles, the speed felt nice. We cruised around the back of Husky Stadium, the runners all keeping a strong pace by now. It wasn't quite so easy for me anymore, or nearly as fun. My thoughts turned to Becky again.

"We're almost there," Paul panted through quick, short breaths. That's when the worst pain came. My high school track coach used to call it "when the bear is on your back." Others call it "hitting a wall." Either way, it really hurts.

"Not now!" I heard myself scream as my legs began to freeze up. Pain shot through them like knives, my lungs were on fire, and I was gulping for air. I wanted to stop, and it took every ounce of mental strength I had not to.

"Kathy, are you okay?" Paul called over to me. Tears stung my eyes. I knew Paul could see the pain in my face.

I looked up to the sky. "God, I need you now! I can't do this, Becky needs you, we need you, please, God help me . . . for Becky." I knew how Becky had suffered during all the chemo, surgery, shunts, and radiation therapy. She was brave, she was my hero. If Becky could do pain for months on end, I could do pain for twenty-three minutes.

I began to chant, "I love you, Becky. I love you, Becky. I love you, Becky." My legs began to respond. My stride began to quicken again. I felt like a well-oiled machine. My mantra became louder, "I Love You, Becky. I Love You, Becky." I could feel my lips forming the words. I ran faster and began to pass people.

"Kathy!" Paul gasped.

"I can't stop! I love Becky!" I called back.

"You go, Kathy!" Paul cheered.

As I rounded the last corner, my stomach burned, my legs began to go numb, and my arms began to pump harder. I could see the quarter-mile track inside the stadium. Runners around me were cheering me in, and people along the racecourse were waving and smiling. I felt so alive, so amazingly strong, as if I were flying. Some call it a runner's high, that unexplainable meta-reality when this physical endurance test somehow becomes amazingly pleasurable. I had my own explanation. I sprinted in the last 200 yards. I probably wasn't sprinting in reality, but hurling my body forward, arms flailing, legs like rubbery noodles until I crossed the finish line.

"That was incredible!" I heard Paul say from behind me as he clapped his hand on my shoulder.

I spun around and smugly replied, "Thank you!" We gave one another a sweaty hug and basked in our post-race glory. "We did it!" I said. As I looked over at University Hospital, I smiled and was happy that day. "Becky, we made it!"

In the face of an impossible situation, I had a triumph that fed me and gave me hope. I was able to place in a race and bring souvenirs and winnings back to my friend to honor her struggle. Although my dear friend was dying, the memory of her and of her fight would live on. And I would live another day to help someone else. Little did I know it would be our youngest son.

Seattle Dragonslayer

When our son was diagnosed with cancer eight years after Becky's passing, I had to stay at home and provide round-the-clock caregiving because of his immune-compromised health. His surgeon told us about the Northwest Sarcoma Foundation, so I visited their website and read the many stories contributed by other families, as well as the research articles and links that had been provided. I discovered many ways to get involved, including at the organization's annual fund-raising event, the Seattle Dragonslayer.

Contributing to the foundation was a way for me to be a part of something larger than our individual situation and to realize there were others facing similar challenges at different stages. I would caution, however, that some may not be ready to participate in a large event or organization in the midst of personal crisis. Others may draw support connecting with a community of people like them who are dealing with a similar illness. You need to weigh the pros and cons carefully. Some people choose to wait until their loved one is through treatment to participate in the larger community. But just knowing supportive events like these are accessible can be comforting, and referring friends and other family members to them can be quite therapeutic and helpful.

Diane and I scanned the field to find the registration area for the 2009 Seattle Dragonslayer Hike, Bike and Trike. Scores of people clustered in friendly groups trying to stay warm. We'd all gathered on this chilly spring morning to participate in a yearly sponsored walk around Seattle's Green Lake that raises funds and awareness in the fight against the sarcoma family of cancers. There was the scent of fresh earth and new life in the air and the whisper of a breeze. On a banner suspended between two trees, Diane and I read that the Dragonslayer event had been named by a six-year-old sarcoma patient who'd compared his cancer to a dragon. Undergoing a grueling regimen of chemotherapy and radiation was his way of slaying the monster that was trying to take his life.

My son Conner was in the thick of treatments and didn't feel up to attending, but I felt his presence as I roamed the crowd. Diane and I appreciated the beautifully decorated banners that people had made in tribute to loved ones. Some bore photographs; others festive streamers and signs in all colors and patterns. Many people wore team T-shirts, and some families even brought their dogs with brightly colored bandannas tied around their collars to support the family. It dawned on me that some of these children memorialized on the banners had lost their battle to sarcoma.

"Oh no, that little girl died and she was only two," Diane pointed out, her voice trembling.

"I know. Some of these are tributes, not celebrations," I replied, my voice breaking.

After many agonizing months of chemotherapy spent in the hospital with Conner, the grueling surgery and painful recovery, I shuddered, fearful that my own Conner could lose his battle with sarcoma. My stomach twisted as I realized that some had fought bravely and valiantly to a bitter end. How courageous it was for them to be here today.

I couldn't help but imagine what Conner would say if he were here with me. I pictured his worried, protective look and loss for words. But I choked back my tears, pulled myself together, and said to Diane, "We can do this, okay! Our boys are still in this. We can finish this walk today!"

Like me, Diane had spent many long days and nights at Children's Hospital sitting with her son, holding his hand, passing the hours playing card games or laughing with him at a comedy show on TV. Here, surrounded by people who were publicly making a statement to fight sarcoma cancer, we were no longer in the isolation of our individual pain. In that moment, I felt lifted up.

Diane looked me square in the eye and said with deep conviction, "Yes, we can do this. Let's finish this walk."

Arm in arm, we marched straight up to the registration table staffed by volunteers dressed in warm fleece jackets, vests, wool hats, and mittens. An awning shielded them from the rain. Diane and I shared that our sons were battling Ewing's Sarcoma and that we were grateful to have the opportunity to participate in Seattle Dragonslayer.

The registrar who helped us was a young adult osteosarcoma patient, his bald head covered with a stylish black sports beanie. His deep blue eyes shone as he showed us the cartoon book he'd created, starring the superhero Captain Cure who attacked his archenemy, the menace cancer. He talked passionately about his fight with bone cancer, not once, but three times, I silently said a prayer for him and his family.

The young volunteer gladly signed copies of his comic books and posters for our sons and told us to keep fighting no matter what. Thanking him, we promised we would. I shook his hand and lingered for just a moment. We then clutched the pale green T-shirts emblazoned with a white tail he'd given us like prized possessions. I could not know then that he would eventually lose his battle with cancer.

Diane and I made our way to the starting line with the crowds of enthusiastic participants. The master of ceremonies was psyching up the crowd, calling out the names of sponsors and thanking supporters and participants to the loud cheer of the hundreds gathered for the event, their spirits undampened in the misty Seattle rain. The start blast went off, and we were swept up in the sea of people who flowed around the circular footpath of Greenlake's steel gray blue shores.

My pulse quickened and body tingled with anticipation. Diane and I lengthened our strides and found a comfortable walking pace along the outer rim of the path. "Isn't this incredible?" I marveled. A grandmother smiled as she passed us pushing her grandson in a stroller. "We're surrounded by such courage and bravery here," I added.

"Yes," Diane agreed. "I love it." I glanced over at her and saw her eyes brimming with tears.

I thought about my own son. He was the hero who, before cancer, had volunteered after school and on weekends at the Second Chance Wildlife Shelter near our home in Snohomish taking care of sick and injured forest animals. Now each day his bravery shone as he fought to live. Today was an opportunity to share courage, joy, and, yes, even pain.

At the day's end, my emotions were bare and raw. As a caregiver of a child with cancer, I needed to stay strong for my son and keep my emotions in check. He couldn't see me fall apart when he looked to me for encouragement. Most days we were in the midst of treatment, and I'd trained myself to keep from becoming despondent, to see the positive in the smallest things. Walking Greenlake that day gave me a much-needed break from the hospital and the solitude of our home. I saw the bigger picture, the far-reaching cruelty of cancer. My family and Diane's family were fighting it now: it was our new normal. The toll cancer had taken not only on our life but on that of so many others was a reality from which we could never turn away. As we hugged at the finish line, Diane and I were both grateful to be kindred spirits, with a friendship forged on the cancer/caregiver battlefield.

Both of us felt empowered by the knowledge we could do something besides simply sit and watch our sons suffer. We had a voice, and we were not alone. I couldn't wait to share the day's souvenirs with my family. I could not know then that Seattle Dragonslayer would become our family tradition each year. Or that, by now, my son would be one of the fortunate cancer survivors.

Paula's Pillowcase Project

My friend Paula started a grassroots project for crafters and sewers to make pillowcases for the children in Seattle Children's Hospital's oncology floor after her son underwent chemotherapy treatment. She has been doing the project now for six years. Once a year, after gathering up yards of donated fabric, she rounds up loving, caring volunteers to sew their "buns off" for two days at her church.

Paula makes a fun event out of it by creating an assembly-line operation, complete with cutters, pinners, ironers, sewists, and card-makers to assemble these loving pillowcase packets for her recipients. Bakers and cooks are recruited, too, to provide meals and snacks for the volunteers. Everyone gathers for as many hours as they can to contribute to a worthwhile cause while visiting, bonding, and sharing! Conner still has his pillowcase from this event.

Some people feel compelled to action, feel energized to get out there and be with others who share a similar cause. Often the Internet is an invaluable resource to connect you with organizations that support your loved one's illness or charity. Most hospitals have staff social workers, care providers, or care centers that have access to organizations and foundations that fund-raise and promote awareness. Local organizations, volunteers, places of worship, and community centers will also network and advertise through your newspaper and local hospital. It can be very empowering to get involved, to become a part of the larger community, to fight your cause together, and to give something back as you solicit money for a cure and support for others like your loved one and family.

How Can I Get Out There?

♥ Ask friends and family if they know of any ongoing community events that they currently participate in that champion your cause—then join at whatever level works for you.

♥ Talk to your medical team about any recent or local events (fund-raising, informational, community-building) that are ongoing near and around the hospital and community and step forward to be part of it.

♥ Do an Internet search on the topic of your loved one's particular illness and community events that pertain to it.

11

PET THERAPY

It's well known that animals make wonderful companions, increase a person's self-esteem, and can help fight off depression. Our two black pugs, Dillon and Dublin, and our Norwegian forest cat, Twister, have always brought great joy to our household. When cancer struck our home, they brought so much more. Our pets remained constant and gave us a sense of normalcy. Our four-legged friends shared our good and our bad days. They didn't inquire how Conner was feeling when he became bald or a tube appeared in his nose. They didn't complain about the long hours they were quarantined at home due to Conner's weakened immune system.

One late afternoon, we had just returned home from the hospital utterly exhausted. No sooner had I slumped into the couch and Conner fallen back onto the loveseat, than Twister jumped into his lap, wanting to be petted. He rubbed his soft furry face on Conner's hands. At first, Conner gazed down at Twister with tired eyes, his skin pale and drawn. But soon Conner began to gently pet Twister's smooth tawny fur as our cat purred in appreciation. Dillon and Dublin crawled up next to me, their adoring black eyes looking into my own as they let me bury my fingers deep within their soft black coats. Our tension seemed to evaporate.

Our friends and neighbors appreciated how important our pets were to our family and offered to help us take care of them when we weren't able. Pet walking was scheduled into our Care Calendar twice a day when Conner and I were at the hospital and my husband was away at work. One friend reassured me, "Thanks for giving me the opportunity to help you by letting us walk the dogs for you. That is something I can do." Pet sitting and dog walking allowed friends an enjoyable way to assist our family without intruding in our private suffering.

The seven- and nine-year-old girls next door were our best dog walkers. I remember our door bell ringing in the morning and the giggles as I answered the door.

"Hello Mrs. Opie! Are Dillon and Dublin home? We came over to take them for a walk!" Each girl wore shiny new rubber boots and a matching purple and pink rain parka. Our two wiggling, yipping small black dogs snorted and howled as they ran between the girls' legs. Dublin jumped up for dog kisses as the girls cried out, "Oh, so cute!"

"Thank you! You're our best dog walkers! Dillon and Dublin just love you!" I beamed and reached inside the doorway to get their leashes.

Decorating the Hospital Room with Pet Photos

When Conner was admitted to the hospital, I taped photos of our dogs and cats, along with the pictures of our family, to covered posters and then attached them to the cupboard space in his room. Our pets' furry, cute, sometimes goofy faces brought joy and familiarity to an otherwise stark, sterile room. A healthy boy and a pre-cancer family smiled back at us in those photographs, giving us a temporary respite from our current hardships and hopes for a better time.

The hospital staff loved our "Rogues Gallery." One young nurse laughed out loud after she discovered the picture of Dublin covered in catnip, her head sticking out of a hole in a cat tree post. "Is this your dog?" she asked. "That is hilarious. You've got to meet the head nurse. She loves pugs. Me . . . I like golden retrievers. I have one at home."

Conner pushed himself up onto his elbow and replied thoughtfully, "My mom is crazy about pugs. We used to have a black lab, Comet. Now he was a cool dog! That picture over there is my granddad's lab." He pointed over to a photo taken during his summer trip to visit his grandparents.

The young nurse replied, "Labs are wonderful dogs, too." She walked over to take a closer look at the collection of pictures before leaving the room. It was a welcome change of topic and lightened our mood for a moment.

Pug Therapy

Several years before, my husband's dad, Rob, had taken a turn for the worse and was in the hospital after his wife passed away. He didn't seem to care about much anymore, and his children and their spouses felt quite helpless to help him. I remembered how much Rob loved the family dog and enjoyed our new puppy, Dillon.

I asked the nurse if pets were allowed on the floor and she replied, "We don't allow animals up here, but my shift ends at 2 p.m. And I didn't see a thing."

Later that afternoon, I tucked a small black furry bundle into my pink hoodie as Paul, our children, and several of my father-in-law's brothers and sisters headed up to the fourth floor cardiology unit for what we affectionately called "pug therapy." We all tiptoed off the elevator and into the room, glancing sideways up and down the hallway to make sure nobody saw us. I unzipped my hoodie and placed the little puppy on Rob's chest.

"Oh, what have we got here?" Paul's dad exclaimed and lit up as he cradled the dog in his arms. Rob looked all around and kept saying, "They brought me a puppy, I have a puppy visiting me here." Everyone stood around smiling, basking in Rob's happiness, the room glowing with love and warmth.

Two Pugs and a Cat

Animals are therapeutic for people during illness, and pet therapy is now acknowledged to have a positive effect on patients. There are specially trained therapy dogs that visit hospitals regularly and are known to have great success in helping adults and children feel better.

Our family also found this to be true, although our pets were only with us while Conner convalesced at home. We received permission from our son's oncologist for our dogs and cats to stay with our family, as long as no new animals were introduced. We weren't able to allow friends to bring their pets over to visit. Not all pets are equal: Conner's pet gecko, Grace, had to stay with a friend during his treatment because reptiles carry salmonella. Conner's immune system was so weak that exposure to any germ could be devastating. Nobody could come to visit nor could we leave home. During our periods of quarantine, our animals came to our rescue, distracting and entertaining us before we could tire of one another.

One morning, I decided to make things fun. I set out a paper shopping bag and a large cardboard box in our family room for the cat to play in. From the couch, Conner and I watched the show unfold. Twister gingerly approached the bag, stalking his new domain in great anticipation, twitching his fluffy tail. As he delicately chose each step, he began the hunt. Twister would pounce upon the unsuspecting paper bag and jump several feet in the air as the bag rumpled and crackled.

"OH no, this bag is ALIVE! What cruel, terrible joke is THIS?" I voiced over for Twister. His green almond eyes grew wide and he circled back around. I looked back at Conner, delighted to see he was engaged in the follies, his eyes alert and his previously slumped body sitting upright, watching, interested.

"You're not getting away that easily, BAG. You are prime real estate!" I growled and meowed for emphasis as Twister jumped inside the paper bag in triumph. I looked back to see the slight smile that spread across my son's face. It was the first smile I'd seen in weeks.

Not wanting to miss out on any attention, Dillon and Dublin stopped by to inspect what all the commotion was about. Twister sat proudly in the entrance to his new hiding spot. The dogs snuffled about and then poked their wrinkled pug faces inside the bag. Conner and I laughed deeply and loud. For a while, he could forget his fight with cancer. In this moment all he knew was the joy he felt watching the buffoonery of two pugs and a cat.

Playing with our pets offered some of the rare moments when Conner laughed and was happy. Because he laughed so seldom now, these refreshing outbursts helped us remember the boy he had been and encouraged us to hope for better days when laughter would come into our home once more.

A Cuddle before Chemo

Pets have a sixth sense and an ability to read our emotions, often before we realize them ourselves. They have been known to position themselves to protect their owners before a catastrophe or warn them of impending danger. They also sense when people are sick. Pets will come to them to ease their suffering.

Conner dreaded going to the hospital. It meant pain, nausea, and poisons being pumped throughout his body. He didn't have to say anything; we all knew how he felt. His way of coping was to tune out and try to sleep through most of it.

We had a routine the morning of each chemo admission. On one such morning, I entered his room to wake him before I prepared our overnight bags and made sure the house was in order.

"Hey, Sweetie, it's almost time to go," I said softly and swept my hand across his smooth, bald forehead.

"Unh-huh," Conner grumbled and slumped over, trying to ignore me. I stood patiently until, a few moments later, he stumbled out of his bed. I watched him amble down the stairs still in flannel pajama pants, soft old T-shirt, and a comfortable throw blanket that he'd wrapped tightly around his shoulders. I followed him into the family room and watched him as he curled up on the couch and napped until it was time to leave.

I walked into the kitchen to wipe down the counters and, when I turned to check on him, I noticed that our pug Dublin had tucked herself in by his bald head. She sat on top of him like a hat, and Twister nestled himself at Conner's feet. I smiled to myself. I believed they came to comfort and soothe Conner before he left.

If it's possible to have your animals with you while your loved one is ill, the benefits can often outweigh any inconvenience. Time with animals helps decrease depression in patients and provides companionship.

Later in Conner's treatment, as he continued to get stronger, I used the need to walk the dogs as a reason for both of us to get outdoors for brief periods of time. These outings helped lift our spirits and gave us some necessary physical activity. I found that with their affection and antics, our pets also provided Paul and me additional support, which helped us better care for our son.

I Want a New Pet

We knew Conner was getting better when he insisted on a new pet. I think he wanted to be able to nurture and give back for all the times he had received care. This desire also gave him hope and a goal. One evening after dinner, later in his treatment, Conner came downstairs and bargained with us for a new dog. I smiled at this request because it meant he saw himself post-cancer and that was a huge step forward. With two dogs and a cat already in our household, introducing a third dog into our tiny yard would be nearly impossible.

"Our dogs would have a fit. But what about a cat? Twister could use some company. You could get a new kitten when this is all over. What do you think of that?" I asked, knowing he'd much rather have a new puppy.

"I really want a lab like Comet," Conner said, referring to our former black lab that had passed away several years earlier. "I mean—I just lived through cancer and all . . ." He looked at us with big, sad eyes.

His maneuver nearly worked, but I said, "Don't even go there. We can't do it. But a kitten, a cute little kitten—you like cats, right? We can handle that." Conner's face softened slightly.

"Okay, Mom, you win again," Conner reluctantly agreed. "But it has to be gray and fluffy!"

"Next time we're in clinic, we'll talk to the medical team about getting you a new pet," I said, relieved he had conceded so easily.

I brought up Conner's wish for a new pet with our nurse practitioner later that week at the hematology-oncology clinic. She explained because his immune system was still compromised, Conner wouldn't be allowed any new pets for the first three months following completion of his chemotherapy.

Conner worked the math in his head and blurted out, "So, September 21 is when we can go to the animal shelter and pick out my new kitten, Mom!" Five months later, on the exact date, we visited the Bellevue Humane Society and helped Conner rescue a small gray Norwegian forest cat. "Hey look, Mom, there's two of them way in the back corner," Conner said and pointed to a group of cages containing several gray and black kittens. I stepped carefully onto the rubber matting to join Conner and his older brother, Patrick. They were in front of the cages and were cooing at the wee cats. Conner held out his finger and wiggled it to see if one of the kittens would approach.

I quickly realized I needed to ask for help and made eye contact with the Humane Society volunteer who graciously turned to help.

"So you're thinking of adopting a kitten today?" she asked warmly and crouched down to speak to my sons.

"Yes, I'd like to see this one," Conner said and pointed over to a small gray kitten who was mewling from the corner. The woman reached in and placed the warm furry ball into Conner's hand. He tenderly cradled the small cat in his palms and smiled up at me. That was our first meeting with Misha. She's now three years old, and this beloved silky cat follows Conner everywhere.

Working with animals after his cancer treatment was over helped Conner rebuild and reshape his life. After treatment, patients can often become despondent trying to re-create their lives, often finding it quite difficult to return to the same activities or sports they once found enjoyable and defining. Before cancer, Conner had worked in an animal shelter. After, he was still able to do his work at a local veterinary clinic. His skill set from his previous volunteer work transferred, and he was able to bring comfort and hope to frightened and pain-wracked animals in ways that few could. The flipside was that, the animals didn't ask about his cancer, if he was scared that the cancer would come back, what the effects of chemo brain (chemically induced attention deficit disorder, which can last months, years, or be permanent) were, or what daily aches and pains he experienced. He cared for the animals and they cared back. At home, taking care of animals instead of receiving care was truly liberating and therapeutic for our son. It helped Conner heal and become whole again.

Not every pet can handle the demands of an ill person. It is important to find a pet that matches the needs of a loved one. We discovered that our pug Dillon could smell the chemotherapy drugs and feel Conner's illness. He treated Conner as a weaker member of his pack and would growl at him at times. You also need to have enough resources to be able to take care of the animal, while still attending to the primary needs of your loved one.

If you are not immune compromised, there are volunteer groups such as therapy dog groups and "Pet Partners" who will bring trained pets who are well-suited to visit with patients in or out of the hospital. If your doctor will not allow exposure to animals during treatment, there are ways to engage in watching darling live kittens and puppies at play via online kitten cams or puppy cams.

There are also shows dedicated to wildlife in their natural habitat, from eagles to zebras. Our pets helped Conner heal. They were instrumental in our entire family surviving a terrible ordeal.

Pet Therapy

- ♥ Ask your primary care provider if your loved one can have pets with him or her during treatment. Some species, like reptiles and birds, cannot carry too many germs.
- ♥ Enlist help from friends with caring for your pets during illness.
- ♥ When you cannot be with your pets, post pictures of them in places such as the hospital room.
- ♥ Research volunteer organizations who bring therapy dogs to visit while the patient is in the hospital and schedule a visit.
- ♥ Consider the option of having the cancer-free patient or you, the caregiver, volunteering in an animal shelter or veterinary clinic after treatment.
- ♥ If your loved one is not allowed to be exposed to animals, help him or her tune in to cable TV networks such as *Animal Planet* or to the thousands of interest, fun, and engaging animal videos that have been posted online.

12

Therapeutic Options for the Caregiver

In time, you may come to realize that you can't continue the level of caregiving you're providing without some outside help for you. You can find professional support and therapy from a number of sources. Hospitals often provide social workers and support staff for patients and their families. There also may be resource centers set up within the hospital with directories for nearby therapists and local groups who specialize in your particular area of need. Lastly, you may find it beneficial to network with other caregivers and form your own support group.

You may only need a few sessions with a licensed therapist in an individual or group setting, or you may be diagnosed with situational depression and require medication to endure the demands and pressures of caring for a loved one with a serious or terminal illness. What is important is that you get the help you need so you can continue in your role as a caretaker to the best of your ability—and preserve your own health while doing so.

Calling the Hospital Social Worker

I soon realized I was more agitated about Conner's upcoming surgery than I was letting on. I knew I needed to talk with a professional, someone who would keep my words private and help me deal with the feelings that were bottling up inside me. I certainly couldn't share them with my family because I wanted to remain strong and positive. To do otherwise would have added stress to my child and might have impeded his treatment and recovery. The burden on me to maintain my outward composure was becoming unbearable. I decided to call the hospital social worker for help and advice.

As I reached to pick up the phone to make my appointment, I wrung my hands and paced nervously.

"Hello. My name is Kathy and my son is being treated for Ewing's Sarcoma. His tumor removal is in three weeks," I explained and tried to remain calm about our situation. But I knew my shaky, rapid speech was betraying my in-charge façade. Looking back, I realized the social worker was accustomed to such calls.

"Is there anyone I can talk to, someone who has gone through this surgery before? I met another mom in the hospital, but her son is only a few weeks ahead of us in treatment," I continued.

"It's wonderful you're reaching out. Call me Wendy." The social worker tried to reassure me and added, "There's a mother whose son also had Ewing's Sarcoma. He is now about two years out of treatment." Wendy's voice was peaceful and soothing.

I thanked the social worker and made an appointment to talk with her in person during Conner's next chemotherapy admission. During our appointment, I spent nearly ninety minutes sharing my feelings of fear, isolation, and anger over Conner's cancer diagnosis. Wendy was affirming and understanding. She didn't try to fix our problem or find answers. She heard my raw emotions and then asked open-ended questions, allowing me to reflect and think about solutions to some of my dilemmas. I shared how difficult it was to find other parents to talk to on the oncology unit. There were many families dealing with cancer, as well as so many different kinds of cancers, all of which had different treatments and prognoses.

Starting a Caregiver Support Group

Networking with other caregivers who face the same challenges can help you cope with your emotional pain as well as give you useful, practical caregiving tips. For many types of illnesses, there are established support groups you can join right at the hospital or within the community. For those who live in more remote areas, online options such as Skype will help you connect.

In my case, a group of five moms, enough to form a small cancer support group for mothers whose children either have or have had Ewing's Sarcoma, decided to gather once a month. We met in a nearby quaint restaurant, away from the hospital, where we bonded by sharing stages of our cancer journey. You may choose instead to meet in someone's home or, if your group is larger, find a donated retail or community-center space. Many libraries have such spaces available, as do neighborhood centers. Our group has since expanded into including all sarcoma cancers and one of our members Karen, became the regional director of the Northwest Sarcoma Foundation for a time and the working leader of our group.

When Depression Hits

It was spring and late in Conner's cancer treatment. The weather had turned sunny in gray, rainy Seattle. I began opening up the windows in the house. I had to confess, though, I was happier when it was raining. I thought if we had to be stuck in a hospital room or inside our home in quarantine to protect Conner's weakened immune system, I'd rather be rained in. I welcomed the slick gun-barrel gray skies and drizzly rain over a clear blue sky as it matched my mood. *Why should anyone else be outside enjoying a sunny day?* I thought. My reality at the time was a melancholy one. Looking back, I was in a state of deep depression. It would be two years before I finally smiled when the sun came out.

It seemed the nearer our family got to the end of Conner's treatment, the more exhausted everybody had become. Our reserves were shot. Patience had run out, and everyone was beyond fatigue. The platitudes and sentiments that people offered us had worn threadbare and no longer consoled us. Plus, we'd called in nearly every favor we could and felt like we were living in a state of perpetual neediness. It was a terrible place to be. I heard the continual drumbeat of, "Aren't you so happy this is almost over?" and "You must be just thrilled your son is cured from cancer?"

Yet "happy" and "thrilled" were words that hardly described the used-up, washed-out person I had become. How could I possibly begin to respond to those comments, other than with insincere superficialities: "Oh yes, we're thrilled, so very happy!"

But why wasn't I happy? Why couldn't I fathom what happiness felt like? Shouldn't I be ecstatic? If the final scans came back clean the following month, we would have succeeded in conquering the demon, dragon monster. Our son would be considered cancer-free. But all I wanted to do was lie down in a corner and sleep for six months, or a year, and cry for weeks. But nobody ever tells you that part of the story.

And then there was my guilt. So many people had stepped forward to help in countless ways, even strangers, so why wasn't I incredibly grateful and appreciative? In my quiet moments, I was angry and resentful that our former life had been taken from us without warning, that we were no longer unaware of the horrors that can ravage a young body. I felt hollow, and our long struggle seemed terribly unfair.

What was wrong with me? I wondered. I withdrew and avoided people just as Conner had been doing all along. I was, in fact, deeply depressed, a completely normal reaction to the terrible ordeal that our family had just survived. I wish someone had been there to explain this to me at the time. When our son finished treatment, the crisis was over. But now I had the time to truly reflect and react to what had just happened to our son, and to our family, over the last ten months.

Although the days were trying while Conner was undergoing treatment, we were able to keep busy with the day-to-day tasks of caregiving. Now that we were able to return to our regular lives, I realized that our old lives would never again be the same. Ours was "a new normal" our care professional explained, whatever that meant. It would take time to heal, to grieve, and to accept that I was a different person now, one whose trust and optimism had been shaken. Looking back, I should have sought help sooner. Eventually, I reached out and saw a therapist who diagnosed me with depression. I took antidepressants for a year to help me through the toughest emotions and the post-traumatic stress that I was experiencing. To learn from my example, don't wait until the stress becomes unbearable for you. The last thing you want to feel when you are in the midst of a patient's treatment or celebrating his or her recovery is depression.

When You Must Grieve

For those who are about to or have just lost a loved one, finding grief support can be essential. When I realized my dear friend Becky was dying of breast cancer, I had to cope with my feelings about impending loss. I chose to attend a grief support group at Evergreen Hospital in Kirkland, Washington. After Becky died, I called upon my church to have a lay minister trained in grief counseling come and visit me at my home each week for several weeks to help me work through my feelings after her death. What follows is the story of my experience with a grief support group.

To be strong for my friend, I was going to get support and help. Instead of thinking of this as a sad event, I was trying to think of it as a positive one. As I arrived, I noticed this hospital area looked like a friendly and warm place, not sterile or antiseptic as I imagined such a place would be. The softly lit halls, newly carpeted and covered with soft pastel-shaded artwork, lulled me to relax. I entered the social services wing and sat down in a soft armchair in the waiting room. A gentle-voiced receptionist offered me a clipboard and some paperwork to fill out before the meeting began.

There were about ten of us gathered for the meeting. I searched the room and its contents, trying to draw any parallels between it and the room where Becky and I had first met. We had first met in a support group for abused children. This hospital venue was definitely higher end, with new fixtures, seating, and paint. There were men and women of varied ages—mostly professionals—and most had a deep look of determination, save for a few bewildered souls. I figured the latter were "newbies," people just learning about cancer, not seasoned veterans like some of us for whom the shock and uncertainty had been erased by experience and resignation. I couldn't believe how far the hand of cancer reached.

It amazed me to see so many stages of grief represented in the same room. It was at once comforting and horrifying. There were husbands whose wives were struggling to cope with the news, mothers of daughters and sons grappling to survive cancer, cancer patients themselves learning to cope with their torturous treatment regime. Then there were others, like me, who were trying to run away from the death sentence that had been passed down to their friends and families.

The counselor listened tenderly, even eagerly, to each person's heart-wrenching story, then pulled it together into a sensible, even plausible, summation, all without shedding a tear or breaking down. Her equanimity was calming. I looked around the room, wondering how many loved ones would survive and how many wouldn't. Unlike our professionally trained counselor, my heart began to break again and again.

At the end of the session, which seemed to come so quickly, I was amazed how close all these strangers felt to one another. The counselor offered us juice and cookies, simple comforts that tasted wonderful. It was healing to be guided beyond bitterness by a seasoned therapist.

Therapeutic Options for the Caregiver

- ♥ Investigate if you need professional therapy and/or medication for help with depression. Talk with your doctor or psychiatrist about this.
- ♥ Ask your hospital family center or hospital social workers to recommend grief or cancer support groups that meet in your area.
- ♥ Look for online groups that support your particular cause or interest.
- ♥ Think about networking with other caregivers to start your own support group or join a group or activity where you can gain support from other caregivers like yourself.

13

WHEN MEN ARE CAREGIVERS

S everal of the men I interviewed had their first caregiving experience as a parent of a sick child. I asked them what was helpful, what was challenging, and how they recharged. Their perspective was different from that of the men who were taking care of an elderly parent or parent in-law. A marked difference between the two groups was that the parents' emotional pain and stress in caring for afflicted children was more acute than that of the adult children caring for aged parents.

My husband cared for his elderly father during his final days. Paul understood how things would progress and knew his job was just a matter of making his dad comfortable. When his father was lucid, the two of them would talk about the old days: these were fun and rewarding times. Other times, Rob would become confused and incoherent, and it was challenging for my husband. Often his father's state was somewhere in between.

One favorite shared pastime for them was watching old westerns together. Eventually, Paul's father couldn't separate fantasy from reality. The TV villain became real for Rob, and he would grow increasingly agitated, often hours after the show ended. In an attempt to ease his father's distress, Paul's sister suggested a favorite 1970s sitcom, *Barney Miller*, which had enough drama and social issues to keep his dad engaged, but that provided a light comic edge that wouldn't upset him. The only problem was, Rob's attention span was ten minutes long, and his hearing was nearly gone. Paul fondly remembers his father watching the same episode three times a day and at high volume. It was a small price to pay to keep him happy in his final days.

The practical skills my husband, Paul, learned while caretaking his aging father transferred readily to our son's care, especially post-surgery. I was amazed at how easily Paul was able to transfer Conner to and from the bed or the restroom using strong, yet delicately careful movements. When our son was in pain, he seemed calmer and more familiar with what to do than I. Paul's prior experiences with his dad had better prepared him for his caregiving role with our son Conner.

Paul found his teenage son more emotionally difficult to reach than his aged father. Conner didn't want to talk or visit when Paul cared for him. During treatment at Seattle Children's Hospital, they would often play a video game together for about an hour. But after that, our son would simply withdraw and sleep. He rarely watched TV, with the exception of one sitcom that would usually elicit a laugh from him. Paul said he knew he was doing his job of sitting and comforting his son while he rested, but Conner's suffering and anger were beyond his reach for a time.

Paul recounted for me a fond memory from these uncertain days. "It was the night after I was driving back from Conner's first diagnosis at Seattle Children's. I had met you there, so we had two cars to drive home. Conner wanted to drive home with me. As we drove up 45th Street past Greek Row at the University of Washington, we saw two very attractive young ladies walking to a Halloween party. One was dressed as a devil and the other as an angel. As we drove past, Conner quipped, 'I can't wait to go to college.'" As he spoke, Paul smiled and said Conner's comment brought him much comfort because it helped him look ahead to his son's recovery and made him realize that Conner, too, believed he would get better.

One man I interviewed said that taking care of his ninety-eight-year-old father-in-law didn't require the technological skill or attention to detail that his job did. Instead, it required more empathy and understanding, as well as overlooking the mistakes that his father-in-law, Ulrecht, made over and over again. As he reflected back on his sixteen years of helping Ulrecht, Al felt he had become a gentler, more introspective person. "In many ways, taking care of a ninety-eight-year-old, is like raising a child," he said.

When I asked him how caregiving made him feel, he spoke of the need to pay constant attention to Ulrecht's needs, to redirect Ulrecht's attention when necessary, and to have a good sense of humor while doing so. Al also said he felt like more of a "life-giver" than a caregiver and that the dog and cat helped both him and his father-in-law a great deal by providing entertainment, affection, and distraction.

The men I interviewed found deep satisfaction in their caregiving roles and were able to provide comfort and companionship to their loved ones. Several of the men revealed that they often found it especially difficult both to ask for and to accept help from others. These male caregivers did not reach out for social interaction to find comfort or reassurance as often as women did. Yet, my husband did share his feelings of grief and powerlessness with a coworker, Brian, during our son's cancer. He gave Paul his gold cross to wear. It was to become a symbol of faith and of their solidarity in friendship. This kind gesture touched Paul deeply. He often spoke of the gold cross and wore it until the day Conner's treatment ended.

How Male Caregivers Coped

In our interviews, three major themes emerged that helped these men navigate their experiences: maintaining a sense of normalcy, exercise, and spirituality. The value of each applies to caretakers of any kind.

Maintaining a Sense of Normalcy

Cancer turns your world upside down. It's important to try to maintain a sense of normalcy for balance and sanity. Some of the activities the men engaged in were entertaining their child's friends who came to visit, attending a sibling's baseball game, grabbing a Starbucks coffee, talking to people outside of the family, going for a long drive together as a family when the child's health allowed, or working on homework together. Participating in favorite pre-cancer activities that were still possible for both caregiver and child allowed them time outside of the illness and hope for a life after illness.

Most of the men I talked with weren't the primary caregivers. This allowed them time to leave the hospital and work at their jobs. Work gave them other responsibilities and a focus outside of caregiving. It also showed them that life keeps moving forward, even when there were setbacks or difficult days at home. For several of the male caregivers, their work brought a sense of relief, comfort, and routine.

"I needed to work. I know that my work is a big part of who I am. I needed to go to work to keep sane," said one father.

"Because I had to work, I had to keep a somewhat normal routine. I think that the more I was able to keep the pre-cancer routine, the more stable and balanced I felt and the easier it was to return to caregiving," another said.

One of the male caregivers was the primary caregiver and didn't have work as an outlet. His perspective was, "Be prepared to give up your work commitments. Take a leave. Otherwise the stress and unpredictability of life in the cancer ward will destroy you."

Regular Exercise

Most of the male caregivers felt that taking time to run or work out at the gym was a good way to relieve stress and take a mental break from the pressures of caregiving. The added benefit of a boost to physical and mental health from exercise was also important to them.

"I would go for a run and get out of that friggin' hospital as often as possible," one dad confided. "I started doing a circuit training class at 6 a.m. to get my head clear before the rounds of doctors descended on the room."

Some caregivers are faced with a terminal situation where time is limited and taking precious moments away from a loved one is not an option. One such caregiver mentioned that his escape time was writing in a journal while his child slept. Writing is mental exercise and can give an emotional release. As well, it can help a caretaker record sensations and experiences that he can reflect upon at a later date.

"One thing that did help me," explained Kiyo, father of a terminally ill son "was many nights sitting next to Josh, simply blogging on CaringBridge. (CaringBridge is a free online blog for friends and families to keep in touch and stay updated during a life-threatening illness.) Josh's presence helped me put many things in perspective."

Kiyo's CaringBridge entries were prolific and inspiring to all who had the privilege of reading them. Through his self-reflection, raw honesty, and heartfelt entries, Kiyo helped many people. Every few days, he would update his blog, sometimes focusing on particularly tough topics. Kiyo shared his deepest emotions with wisdom and generosity as he invited readers into the family's daily world with Josh.

Kiyo's son was an incredibly gifted and dedicated baseball player. Kiyo had helped coach his son's team, and the whole family loved the game. Josh played until he was no longer physically able because, for Josh, there was no other option. The following is from Kiyo's journal entry about Josh's high school baseball team rallying behind him.

> *Josh was at the game. Watched most of the game until finally fatigue from radiation set in. But he heard it. Loud and clear. His teammates, huddling by the first base foul line. Instead of typical "IRISH" cheer, they all got together, and simultaneously . . . and clearly and loudly said . . . "JD". Even now several hours after the game, I can still hear it and gives me goosebumps. Watching and hearing, even when Josh was not in the dugout, they are there for him."*
>
> —Kiyo, CaringBridge: May 16, 2012

Toward the end of his son's ordeal, Kiyo wrote of his family's decision to place Josh in hospice for palliative care that would ease his son's suffering as he died. Reading the entries, his community of followers experienced the love and deep connection that help soften even the worst sorrow. Until Josh's final day and even after, Kiyo kept his community informed. Josh was incredibly courageous, someone who never quit on the ballfield, in the hospital, or on friends or family. One of his favorite quotes was "Stubborn gets shit done." Yet finally, Josh couldn't take the pain any longer. The cancer had finally overtaken his body. Here, Kiyo bravely, poignantly, and openly shares a final time with his son.

> *As I sit in RM 3293 of Seattle Cancer Care Alliance at Children's, I watched our boy doze off for good. Peaceful and with relaxed face, snoring at times. Josh no longer feels pain . . . I am also at peace knowing he is finally comfortable. Finally.*
>
> —Kiyo, CaringBridge: July 24, 2012

Spirituality

One of the men I interviewed explained, "I found it very calming and peaceful to go down to the hospital chapel to pray or just sit and meditate in a spiritual setting." Others would take a walk outside and find a peaceful place to meditate or reflect. They described this time as renewing for them: it gave them a fresh perspective and the encouragement they needed to return to their responsibilities. Some of the men would also attend a service at the hospital chapel, taking comfort in guided worship. Overall, spending time alone in reflection and prayer brought these men much-needed solace and comfort.

Life Lessons Shared

Experiencing a child's life-threatening illness or death changes us forever. It's certainly something none of these men expected. "To face losing a child is something no parent should have to do," one of the men said simply. At the other end of the caregiving spectrum is taking care of an aging parent who is in decline or terminally ill. Although this is an expected part of life and doesn't carry the weight of disbelief and shock that a child's illness does, this, too, requires one to dig deep into one's reserves of time, energy, and compassion. Through their caregiving, the men I interviewed learned many valuable lessons. Their honest and powerful self-reflection gave them hard-won insights that they shared freely.

- ♥ Take one day at a time: By coping with what is directly in front of you, you can avoid being overwhelmed with daily thoughts of the upheaval you and your family face.

- ♥ Don't look for trouble by self-diagnosing your loved one. Let the experts do that for you. Although you can find research on your child's illness online, you may encounter conflicting information. The medical experts working directly with you and your loved one are the most trusted sources for information when you need it.

- ♥ Your story is yours to handle in your own unique way; don't compare yourself to others. For example, some families may be quite vocal about their loved one's treatment; some will even be in the public eye with their particular story. Other patients and their families don't want much attention. It is okay to decline from talking about your situation if you aren't comfortable. You may want to choose only a few close friends with whom you can talk about your feelings. Do what is best for you and your family, and be okay with your decision.

♥ Patients need positive feedback and supportive comments, not sympathy and pity. Let people know when a comment isn't helpful, to give them a better understanding of the patient's situation and state of mind. This will help them avoid repeating insensitive comments.

♥ Well-meaning people may try to reason or justify the unexplainable and difficult situation you are in the midst of with a sweeping statement, such as "It's God's will." The best response to such ill-chosen statements is no response at all.

♥ As a caregiver, it is likely you won't know the outcome of your loved one's treatment for some time. It's wise to appreciate the special and small things that happen day to day and cherish the time you share.

♥ When faced with discouraging odds and sometimes insurmountable obstacles, one man simply stated that he did all he could do, and it was his best effort. This is all you can ask of yourself.

♥ "Hug your kids and your loved ones every day." This quote from Kiyo, who lost his only child, is a very poignant and touching reminder. It makes you want to put this book down right now and get up and hug someone immediately!

♥ When you have lost or face losing a loved one, you realize that no amount of money or possessions can save them or compensate you for the loss. It puts everything into a whole new perspective, showing that material things count very little when measured against a life.

♥ Don't self-medicate when stress hits. Find healthy outlets. For example, it is easy to binge-drink when faced with a life-threatening illness. Alcohol seems to take the edge off of the raw emotions that come from a crisis, but the relief is only temporary and comes with its own set of problems. There are healthier ways to cope, such as exercise, meditation, or reaching out to friends or a support network.

14

SPIRITUALITY AS A SOURCE OF STRENGTH

There may come a time as a caregiver when you feel that you're being tested beyond the limits of your normal coping abilities. Drawing strength from a spiritual source, through prayer or meditation has helped many people persevere during trying times. These difficulties can arise from the day-to-day trauma of a seemingly never-ending illness of a loved one or from witnessing a particularly painful event.

I found spiritual support in the form of prayer or my conversations with God. This was an integral part of my daily caregiving routine and was absolutely instrumental in helping me survive some particularly grueling experiences. My friend Tom, who visited his friend Bob during the last weeks of Bob's life, found prayer to be a source of strength. My friend Kayla connected with the divine through her relationship with nature. Dr. John Neff, former medical director of Seattle Children's Hospital lends his perspective to the value of interfaith spirituality. Their stories illustrate how a strong faith foundation can help during some very trying caregiving times.

Time with God

After visiting my friend Becky one evening, we knew her battle against terminal cancer was near an end. We had tried to say as many last sweet things to one another as her speech-impaired condition would allow. After an especially emotional visit, I had just pulled out of her driveway. Becky had been collapsing since the cancer metastasized. It was impossible for her to walk anymore, even though she refused to quit trying. Watching cancer ravage my friend's body, knowing there was nothing I could do to stop it, had left me beyond exhaustion. I was ready to give up hope.

The pain and anger I felt as I drove away from her house was so overpowering that I challenged the God I believed in so fervently. Why had he allowed this to happen to Becky, to her family, and to everyone who loved her? I demanded an answer. Amazingly, I had an epiphany that included hearing God reassure me that he was with me and had never left. This was followed by a physical warmth that spread throughout my body, creating a deep, peaceful sensation. Although the moment passed, the certainty that my faith would carry me through remained.

Some people regularly turn to spirituality to give them strength, which was Becky's practice. She enjoyed having favorite people read to her from her Bible, or play her favorite worship music from Michael W. Smith's album *Go West Young Man.*

Those of us close to Becky took turns sitting by her bedside every hour throughout the evening hours of her last days. I played "Place in This World" from the album as I held her hand. I thought Becky couldn't hear or see me, but soon her hand began to squeeze mine, rhythmically, every ten to fifteen seconds and her breathing slowed. My friend was comforting me, "her sensitive one," even as she lay dying. Becky's faith kept her strong and able to give back until the very end.

A few years later, when my son got sick, I again relied heavily on my faith in God. I carried a daily devotional, "Pearls of Great Price" by Joni Eareckson Tada, a quadriplegic woman who chose to believe in her faith in God and His plan for her life rather than giving in to self-pity and the limitations of being in a wheelchair. Her inspirational message of positive thinking, perseverance, and prayer gave me encouragement. I also visited the hospital chapel to pray, attended services, or meditated with a friend when I had the opportunity. The next story is about a time when I didn't think I could go on and again called out to God.

I Can't Go On

It was just after Conner's surgery; his right shoulder re-section and tumor removal to be exact. He had been admitted to the hospital for Influenza B. Our whole family had been immunized for Influenza A, but Conner's body, frail and weak from months of chemotherapy and his recent surgery, couldn't fight off the many strains of influenza that were in the environment. His temperature had been climbing and the admitting doctor placed us in an isolation room to protect everyone from the infection. It was the first of many infections Conner would battle. Looking back, I don't know how he made it. I believe none of us was alone: God carried us through.

During the night, I listened to Conner's rhythmic breathing and the humming of his heart monitor and oxygen-level machines. Knowing he was hooked up to the monitors helped me believe everything was going to be fine, that all was under control. But at one terrifying moment, the alarms rang and his blood pressure dropped dangerously low to 80/40.

The nurses burst into the room and swiftly administered lifesaving medicine to him. I bolted upright in bed. Conner hardly stirred; he was too sick. He only coughed, moaned, and slept. I kept vigil over him, praying and thinking of a day when we would no longer need to be here, when our lives would return to normal and our son's life would no longer be in peril or he would no longer be in pain.

The next morning, when Conner was out of danger, I stepped out onto the oncology floor in a sleeplessness-induced stupor and paused a moment to think about the dramas that might be occurring behind the door of each hospital room. Did each child have as rough a night as Conner, or even worse? What were their prognoses? I said a silent prayer for each child and family as I walked by their rooms.

The following week, we were back at the hospital for our pre-chemotherapy appointment. Our nurse decided to give us our final exit plan and Conner learned he would be done with chemotherapy treatment by the third week of June if all went well. I saw Conner's face brighten for the first time in weeks, as he was able to look forward to the possibility of being done.

"After eighteen months, it goes to every six months until three years have passed, and then to once a year until the five-year mark, when you're considered in remission," the nurse continued.

Conner's bubble burst. He just hung his head.

"I'll be in college then!" Conner gasped as the news began to sink in.

"Yes, I know, Kiddo. Welcome to your 'new normal.' This will always be a part of you, even after you've beaten it," she explained simply. At the time, Conner's nurse seemed impersonal. But looking back, she had to be impartial and present a strong front to help Conner and others grasp the enormity of their healing journey. I realized that we probably had been given this information early in treatment, but hadn't had time to process it yet. Everyone needed to remain strong, including the medical staff.

The following week, Conner was back in the hospital to restart chemotherapy. After months of chemotherapy, infections, surgery, and having been told he would never leave the world of cancer, Conner had become extremely emotionally vulnerable.

In the hospital room, Conner and I played UNO and Scrabble. We passed the afternoon joking and talking back and forth. I fooled myself into thinking that perhaps this hospital admission might not be so bad. Maybe Conner's body would rally and, despite his weakened system, he could handle the latest assault of toxins. But the next day, Conner awoke to a vicious bout of nausea, and he threw up his NG tube. The nurses came in and helped clean up the mess while Conner lay moaning. I rubbed his back as he curled up in a tight ball.

"Mom, I just want to die," he cried.

I thought he was joking. I really hadn't sensed his despair accelerate like a freight train heading right toward us. We had just had a good day, I reasoned. Perhaps his feelings of hopelessness were temporary?

"You don't mean that, Honey; it's going to be okay." I tried to soothe my son, desperate to find something, anything I could do to help. I continued to rub his back, knowing this always comforted him.

"No, Mom, I mean it. I can't do this anymore. I just want to die." He looked at me through hollow, dark round eyes. "I feel so sick and so awful. Can't I just die? I don't want to suffer anymore, I can't do this," he cried and fell back into his bed defeated.

The months of pain and suffering, followed by a horrifically painful surgery, topped with weeks of influenza, only to be told by his nurse that it would never truly be over had taken their toll. Conner would have to come back to the hospital again and again, just in case. His spirit was nearly broken and my heart split in two.

But he needed me to remain hopeful and positive. That's where the experience, strength, and wisdom of age and faith give a mature caregiver an edge, especially when dealing with young patients. At this moment of despair, when the pain seemed almost too much for him to bear, I could reassure Conner that this too would pass; that he would survive.

"Conner, things won't always be like this. Look how far you've come and look at the wonderful future ahead! You can make it." I encouraged my son as calmly and soothingly as I could. Once I got him settled down, the nurses managed to get his anti-nausea medications on-board, I rubbed his back for a time, and finally Conner drifted off to sleep.

Watching my son suffer and reach his breaking point nearly broke me. As I looked out of the hospital window that gray, drizzly Seattle winter afternoon, I desperately wanted to be anywhere else. None of my coping strategies—a run, a coffee break, a visit with friends—helped. Inside, I felt utterly alone, despondent, and knew I had desperately few reserves of energy from which to draw.

I silently prayed, "God, I can't do this anymore, not without some help from you. I know people are praying for us, but I can't take this. Watching my child suffer when there's nothing I can do to stop it has to be one of the worst things any parent can endure. I have to draw from Your strength because there's nothing left here." I paused and turned away from Conner so he wouldn't see me cry. "Please, God, if you're listening, send me a sign, anything," I begged.

At that moment, I looked up and saw something outside the window. A small hummingbird was trying desperately to get inside our hospital room. Fat raindrops pelted this little creature, yet it continued to beat its tiny wings fiercely up and down near the tan concrete walls of the hospital. As I watched the small bird flittering before me, the blur of its wings, I remembered reading somewhere that hummingbirds were a sign of hope.

Later, I would learn that hummingbirds are also a symbol of "accomplishing that which seems impossible." My dad would later tell me hummingbirds do not migrate in the winter. The little bird was there on an improbable winter day for a reason. Yes, God was sending me the hummingbird as my symbol of hope. I looked straight up to the sky and whispered, "Thank you, God!" That was the shred of hope I needed to feel reassured that my son would survive.

An Inter-Faith Perspective

It was an unusually balmy spring day as I interviewed Dr. John Neff, former medical director of Seattle Children's Hospital. As we sat on the rooftop garden patio in his downtown Seattle condo, the air was scented with a hint of rose and fuchsia. Interstate-5 traffic rushed below like a river, while the snowcapped Olympic Mountains stood tall and blue-gray Elliot Bay fanned out behind the Seattle skyline. The retired physician was seated comfortably, wearing jeans and a sweatshirt, affably awaiting my first questions.

I wanted to get a perspective on his personal spiritual background as well as learn more about Seattle Children's Hospital's philosophy as a whole. I was excited to make Dr. Neff's acquaintance. At age eighty-two, still brimming with vitality, he'd held more titles and positions than most people I'd ever met.

"So, John, tell me a little about yourself and your background," I began, as I folded open my notebook and poised my pen, ready to scribble my notes.

John smiled and began to speak thoughtfully. "My family has more missionaries than teachers, and my father didn't like dogma of any kind. He felt his goal was to search for the commonality in everybody's beliefs. He didn't like people who preached or proselytized their religion, and instead admired those who strived to live the best life they could. My mother, on the other hand, was more into the ceremony, open praying, and stories of her Christianity. As a physician, I borrowed more of my father's approach to spirituality and came to value everyone's beliefs."

He went on to explain, "The chaplaincy is very broad and supportive at Children's Hospital. We help people find the pastoral care that's most supportive of what their basic belief system is." He cautioned that it would be terribly damaging for any individual or institution—especially a healing institution—to attack the pillars of anyone's belief system, especially by trying to convert someone to a mainstream religion. "People tend to dig down very deep into their belief system once they have experienced a traumatic event, like the serious illness of a child," John continued. "We want to include likeminded people and invite other churches in to help the families feel that they are not alone. It is important to honor, acknowledge, and support spirituality for the individual strength it gives them."

Spirituality can bring a sense of hope during this very trying time. "Children will feel that strength come from the family. They pick it up like a magnet. Also older children will pick up what they like and discard what they don't like," John explained. We went on to discuss why the hospital's chaplaincy is so central during the time of illness and how families draw together in a spiritual setting to receive a sense of "solidarity, community, beyond their earthly presence and beyond themselves."

Since the 1980s, Seattle Children's hospital, like many other medical institutions, has expanded its spiritual support resources. This expansion is based on the recognition that loss and grief are part of a continuum and that a healing experience can go on for a very long time for the family. John continued by saying that when a child dies, families go through another process of questioning and emptiness. Although Seattle Children's Hospital extends its support throughout a patient's treatment and long after, it's important to build on support systems outside of the hospital, especially spiritual ones.

It was affirming to learn that the hospital's continuing mission was so evolved. In my own worship time at the hospital, I had felt a sense of inclusiveness and acceptance of all faiths. This brought me a sense of peace and comfort during such a critical time in our family's life.

The next story explores a different faith perspective. My friend Kayla believes that we are all profoundly connected by a unity of consciousness. For her, we all belong to a grand order and scheme of things, where there is an interconnectedness among all living things, each of which contains a divine spark. She rejects all human forms of God manifestations and instead sees divinity in all natural things. Before her son became ill, her life was an expression of the divine: she loved all people of whatever faith they held. Her own faith was broad, encompassing Taoism and the Great Spirit of the Native American tradition.

Kayla's Spiritual Journey

After her son was diagnosed with Ewing's Sarcoma, Kayla felt an overwhelming sense of betrayal and rejected her spiritual beliefs entirely. She didn't want to connect, only to survive. "Tally's tumor was so big and in a bad place and Tal just kept getting sicker and sicker. I felt numb and the only thing that worked was medicine, not miracles," Kayla softly said. But there was an edge to her voice, and she held my gaze with pained eyes as she tried to recall that time. "I lost all faith. I felt so hurt and betrayed by what had happened to us, to our son. I was so angry. All I wanted to do was survive and so I rejected my faith for sheer medical science."

"I met these amazing, strong women at the Ronald McDonald House, women of all different walks of faith: Buddhist, Mormon, Mennonite, Catholic, and Muslim women who were all so eager to pray with me and for our family. Their faith was so strong and they had such conviction. They didn't have to take time to talk and pray with me. They were busy women who had their own sick children to attend. But they did. For me, it was an incredible infusion of pan-cultural beliefs that transcended my current level of tolerance and acceptance," Kayla shared, her large eyes transfixed on mine. "I learned that there was a common theme of goodness, forgiveness, service, and love from people of all races, religions, ages, and socioeconomic status."

Kayla looked over at me and patted my arm knowingly. We had prayed together several times on our walks, at the chapel at Seattle Children's Hospital, and during her son's nine-hour surgery. "I wasn't so angry about faith after that." Kayla smiled at me and pulled her hair up into a messy bun; she loved to play with her long honey-colored hair. "I had Shamanic healers praying for us and Native Americans—so many that it became a concentric ripple of prayer and I could feel the healing and sense of community."

Kayla spoke of discovering the power of prayer and the symbols of the divine feminine in the Madonna. "Do you remember the picture you gave me of Mary? I still have it. I just love it," she said fondly. "Do you remember when you prayed with me? I treasured those times and learned, as I faced the thought of losing Tally, that I shared my suffering with a woman who could hold the sadness of losing a son. Mary was and is so strong and beautiful to me. Thank you," she whispered.

Since her son's recovery, Kayla has learned to embrace wisdoms from many faiths. She once again finds her spiritual connection in nature as she communes with the divine during a walk within a grove of old Douglas fir trees or on a mountain hike. In this nature temple, she connects with all that is beautiful and sacred in life. It infuses her with hope and gives her the joy of living in her body.

What follows is a story about my friend Tom. He spent each Tuesday visiting his best friend Bob up until he passed away. Tom's faith was an integral party of his journey with Bob.

Tuesdays with Bob

Tom's old college buddy Bob left a voicemail for him one day and asked him to call back. Tom did and soon the call went from social to serious. Bob had just been diagnosed with an incurable form of abdominal cancer and had been given no more than a few weeks to a year to live.

Tom's instant reaction was to come by, offer prayers, and give Bob a hug. Like many friends in a community, Tom is a very caring man who wanted to be present for his friend during his last days. He felt called to visit Bob weekly. What made Tom's visits with Bob special was the personal foundation rooted in faith that he and Bob shared. Tom drew upon their lifetime friendship and faith to be present for his friend Bob when Bob asked him the more difficult life questions, as well as when he witnessed some pain-filled moments. He was able to find and offer to Bob comfort, peace, and consolation through their shared beliefs.

Tom ended up being able to visit Bob on Tuesday afternoons after the effects of chemotherapy had worn off and before Tom's volunteer hours at a local soup kitchen. The two friends decided to limit visits to one hour so Bob wouldn't get tired. Tom said that whenever he was on his way to Bob's for a visit, he'd first stop at a nearby restaurant, then call ahead to see if Bob was up for a visitor. Tom kept a journal of his visits with Bob and his personal reflections about his feelings that he typed up into a small bound book titled *Tuesdays with Bob*. I quote the following from that:

> *So how does one go about sharing such a journey? I knew that I needed to be inspired and guided by the Holy Spirit. I prayed about my role. Basically it amounts to a lot of active listening. Bob set the agenda and pace. I needed to be attentive to his energy level and stop when he seemed tired, be gentle and lovingly positive and affirming. When I thought that I might interject a new idea or comment, I prayed first. Was it the Holy Spirit speaking through me? If that did not seem to be the case, I said nothing.*

—TOM MAHONEY, TUESDAYS WITH BOB

Tom explained when Bob asked the unanswerable questions like, "Why am I still here?" he was able to say candidly, "Perhaps it's because you have more love to give or to receive; perhaps both. When you have completed that, I'm sure God will call you home as you desire." The two friends visited comfortably at Bob's home and fondly reminisced about the old days.

Tom felt that his visits with Bob were energizing and he felt closer to God as well. "This was holy ground. God's love surrounded us," Tom explained. He recounted that Bob's death and funeral were very difficult for him to get through and admitted that, "[My wife] Theresa helped me with that as we took a couple of extra days at our retirement retreat home in Kingston and just let it sink in." Tom also found writing about his experiences very therapeutic.

"The gifts of story and love bestowed on you by a dying friend through your loving, patient, and reassuring presence can be unique and precious," Tom explains. "If a situation ever presents itself to accompany a friend on his or her journey to death, ask God if this one has your name on it." Yet, he cautions, making this commitment is intense and is not to be entered into lightly.

How Do I Connect with Spirituality?

Praying, meditating, finding your spiritual connection in nature, or spending time in worship either in solitude or in community may be a source of sustenance for you during caregiving and beyond. The examples that follow are only a few ideas about how you can reach out for the support you need to stay strong during your time of crisis. Each person's spiritual path is unique. You'll draw from the beliefs, traditions, and practices that best answer your needs.

- ♥ Find a chapel or meditation center at the hospital for solitary prayer or for worship services.

- ♥ Ask your social worker to refer you to spiritual support staff or volunteers at the hospital who can come and visit you during your hospital stays.

- ♥ Seek out gardens and quiet areas throughout the hospital grounds. They can serve as ideal areas for prayer and meditation.

- ♥ Join a friend in his or her interfaith worship service if your own faith is not fulfilling all your needs at this time. Reach out for alternative paths of worship such as Buddhism, Native American spirituality, Taoism, etc., to help you find inner peace and strength.

15

AFTER THE HOSPITAL

There's life after the hospital. Unfortunately, it's going to take time and hard work to finish grieving, to let go of prior caregiving roles, and to regain the life you suspended during illness. Each person's journey, how each one handles stress, and the time frame in which he or she does is different. Whether you have lost a loved one or are coping with the aftermath of a severe illness—perhaps your loved one survived, but now has disabilities to deal with—will shape your path to a new life beyond caregiving and treatment.

First, take some time for yourself. You will need to process the losses, whatever you have experienced and witnessed. As you assume your new role, whatever that new role will be—as the parent, sibling, or friend of a cancer survivor, or as one who has lost a loved one to a devastating illness—you'll need time to relearn. Eventually, you'll find your own life again. Understand that the struggles, pain, and your loved one's outcome will always be a part of you. But perhaps you will have become someone more empathetic, emboldened, passionate, and focused in the process. Please remember, you are never alone: many have traveled not the same road but a similar one. There are people along the way who will help, support, and just be there to listen and understand you.

During this time of recovering your life, it's important to rely on a strong core group of friends and community. Don't be afraid to admit there are days when you don't want to cope or deal with your grief. Sometimes it's okay to do nothing at all or, as one friend so aptly put it, to just "be a pile." Ask your friends to get you out of the house to pursue some of the activities that you used to do and to re-enter the community you spent time in before your loved one got sick. Joining support groups or continuing to attend the ones you began while your loved one was ill can be quite healing. Research has proven that attending support groups during and after treatment is beneficial for parents and caregivers. As you talk to others who describe experiences of loss, fear, and doubt similar to yours, your feelings will be validated, and you'll find a sense of comfort and inclusion.

Our cancer mom support group, "Wings" (named by dropping the E from Ewing's Sarcoma), continued to meet monthly for dinner in local restaurants. We took turns checking in to share our stories, struggles, and progress. Others in the group who were farther along on their journey were able to give hope to the moms of kids beginning treatment. This was vital. Six years later, we still meet, although not as often. Sometimes we need to be supportive or encourage one another about upcoming reparative surgeries or some of the unfair lifelong effects of chemotherapy. These after-effects can surface sometimes years later. Sadly, one of our members lost her child to cancer. We were there to comfort her, listen, and offer compassion. We found our group grew in experience to be present for our friend during the profound grief that comes from losing a child. The original members needed to be flexible and accepting as we welcomed new members who arrived with their individual and particular struggles. Each new member changes the group dynamics yet adds more depth and compassion to our meetings.

Our Life after Treatment

My sister Kellie was arriving in a couple of days. I was excited! I hadn't seen her since winter, and she'd be here to offer moral support through Conner's last set of scans and final checkups. Kellie is a registered nurse, so she could understand everything from the medical perspective. If all Conner's final scans and checkups were clear, Kellie and I planned to head up to the mountains for a few days on a getaway. I hadn't been away from Conner, or farther than a sixty-mile radius from the hospital in more than eight months, and it was time for a break.

We were to begin Conner's twenty-four-hour creatinine study at home the next morning at 5:30 a.m., a test that detects protein in the urine to determine if there was any kidney damage. We needed to keep our sample on ice and bring it with us to the hospital for our final scans and tests the next day.

I thought back to our first creatinine study, feeling grateful we had made it this far. At 6 a.m. the morning of our remaining tests, Kellie accompanied us to the hospital for our 7 a.m. appointment. On our docket were a CT scan, bone scan, echocardiogram, EKG, blood work, and dropping off the sample at the clinic. We hoped everything would go smoothly, because if there were problems, chemotherapy would be resumed and Conner's Hickman line would stay put.

We were all quite anxious. Conner chose to tune out—napping or listening to his iPod (a Christmas gift generously donated to him by the Go4theGoal Pediatric Cancer Foundation), most of the day—so I was grateful Kellie was with me. My husband, Paul, who had missed a lot of work lately, had chosen instead to join us for the Hickman line removal surgery in a few weeks.

Kellie was able to answer all my questions about the echocardiogram, explaining which ventricle we were looking at and what valve was doing what. I knew I could've asked the technician, but figured she was busy. I was amazed at how relaxed my sister was throughout the day. She was never flustered or shocked by anything she read or saw. She was a wonderful support, as my nerves were frazzled by the end of the day. I kept my hands busy with my crochet project and various puzzle games, but the waiting and wondering between appointments for the results was excruciating.

Around 3 p.m., we had a final appointment with Chappie (Dr. Conrad) and Conner's nurse Sue. After he glanced over the charts and read out the results of the reports, Chappie exclaimed, "Well, Conner, you're done! Everything turned out fine! You're a free man!" The doctor smiled at Conner and extended his hand to congratulate him. Our collective sigh of relief could be heard throughout the room and our faces shone brightly.

"Just wait. I need to get a picture of you!" I announced happily and asked Chappie, Conner, and his resident to gather by the examining table. They grinned willingly for the picture. This was a happy day! Sue went over his numbers with us and couldn't help but smile at how far he had come since that rueful day eight months ago. I announced that Conner, his dad, and brother were going to the movies tonight, and my sister and I were heading off to the mountains for a few days. "We're out of here!" I cried in jubilation.

"Don't go too far. Remember your Hickman line appointment is on the seventh," Sue teased and again smiled.

Conner replied, "That's the day *I'll* celebrate."

Kellie and I had a wonderful time in the Cascade Mountains. Our cozy cabin was the perfect getaway. The crisp mountain air, peace, and solitude were just what I needed for my frayed nerves and battered soul. Conner and I hadn't been apart since October, and we both desperately needed a break from one another; although I found myself missing him, as if a piece of myself were gone. I think Kellie understood, as she let me talk on and on about Conner, his progress, outlook, hopes, and dreams. She discovered I had an endless supply of energy, perhaps pent-up nervous energy. I repeatedly asked her to join me on hikes, walking trips around the tourist town of Leavenworth, and Lake Wenatchee. We talked for hours about every topic imaginable, leaving no stone unturned. I tried to call Paul several times a day to check in on him and the boys, but they were often out and about, keeping busy and having their own fun.

When we returned home a few days later, I was anxious to ask Conner how he wanted to celebrate the Fourth of July. It would be his first cancer-free holiday in some time. We had had several invitations to celebrate with friends, and I had also offered to take him to a hotel in downtown Seattle where we could watch the big fireworks display from Elliot Bay, but Conner quietly refused, saying he wanted to stay home and light off fireworks in our neighborhood as he always had. I was slightly disappointed—I had wanted to give him the sun and the moon for his first holiday home. In typical Conner style, he wanted to keep it simple and unobtrusive. Again, I had to remember it wasn't about me.

"Okay then, we'll have a barbeque out on the deck and then we'll go up to the hill and light fireworks. I bet Dad would love to take you and Patrick up to Boom City and get you some of the big fireworks, too." I shook my head at my eagerness to give my son who had just survived cancer even bigger explosives.

It was an unseasonably hot Fourth of July in the Northwest. We barbequed our favorite foods out on the grill, including honey-glazed spare ribs, cheeseburgers, and hot dogs, accompanied by red-skinned potato salad, garden-fresh corn on the cob, watermelon, homemade pasta salad, and a patriotic Fourth of July cake—a yellow cake frosted with Cool Whip and decorated like the American flag with red rows of strawberries for stripes and blueberries for stars. Conner, his brother, sister, Paul, and I bowled a lively game of bocce ball out on the lawn. When we all got too hot in the sun, we came inside to continue our competitive streak with the family's favorite board game, Apples to Apples.

The Hickman line removal was scheduled for July 7 at 9 a.m. We arrived at Children's Hospital at about 6:15 a.m. to register for the outpatient surgery. Saying "outpatient" sounded so good. Dr. Hawkins, our oncologist, would perform the procedure. He told us it would only take ten minutes to remove the line. Conner would take longer than that to recover from the anesthesia.

It seemed only moments later we were being called back to the recovery area to see Conner. As Paul and I walked back through the hallway, we weren't sure what we'd find. This usually had been a difficult experience for us. We were taken aback to see Conner acting so loopy and chatty, when normally he was quiet and groggy with pain. I was amused, if not perplexed, to see this side of Conner.

Dr. Hawkins congratulated us and told us he would see us again in three months for Conner's scans. We all shook hands, and I thanked Dr. Hawkins for everything he had done to save Conner's life. Before I started to cry, Paul insisted it was time to take our son home.

Conner seemed to be bouncing off the walls, as he laughed, joked, and tried to tousle my hair after we left the surgical room. We hadn't seen him this happy since before diagnosis. He insisted on walking out to the car, even though he was a bit wobbly on his legs. He chatted the entire way home, asking when he could play soccer, telling us which friends he was going to invite paintballing, wondering when Dad was going to take him jet skiing, and telling us that tomorrow, after the bandage came off, he was going to take the longest, hottest shower ever! Our son was testing out the idea that he was beginning to get his life back again, and I realized so were we.

We arrived home about forty-five minutes later. As we pulled into the driveway, a huge banner hung across the garage door that read, "Congratulations, Conner! You Fought and You Won!" Our front door was covered with big balloons and streamers.

"Look, Conner," I said through tears. "This is for you. You did it!"

"It's okay, Mom, don't cry, it's okay now," Conner smiled.

It had been a long journey. Conner's is a story of survival, and so far we're very blessed. Despite being pronounced cancer-free, he struggled with adjusting to his new life without the complete use of his arm. And he endured a few additional surgeries to repair some of the broken screws from his scapula allograph. He was no longer able to play contact sports, and even running was painful. He began volunteering, while I had to learn not to be overinvolved in his life or to define myself through him. Taking time for myself and investigating what activities and things I might like to do now that I had the time allowed me to enter my new life. It would take time and the support of family and friends to do so fully, but as the months and years went on and his prognosis and health improved, I found it became easier. I eventually began volunteering for a cancer organization called Northwest Sarcoma Foundation, as well as at my church with a marriage support group. Also, our Wings support group continued to be active, and I would meet with friends from the group socially whenever I had the time for friendship and support.

I found such comradery and connection crucial during those tentative months that followed the end of Conner's treatment. For so long, we had been on such a rigorous schedule of appointments and treatments with so many restrictions. Once it was over, I found myself at a loss with our newfound free-dom, rather than feeling happy from being done with treatment. Several of the friends I had made during Conner's chemotherapy treatment became close friends after treatment. They understood my mood swings, my newly acquired pessimism about the fragility of life, and my lack of hesitancy about talking about difficult health and cancer-related topics. I drew closer to some of my oldest and best friends and had to distance myself from others who didn't under-stand that I would never be the same person I had once been. My caregiving role was over, I was healing, and I was also redefining who I was all at the same time.

On more practical notes, we had to prepare our son to make up the year of school he had missed, and so we set up summer tutoring sessions. We also needed to dispose of his medications and medical supplies. We found a volun-teer organization who took supplies for low-income families. We also set up a payment plan through the hospital finance department for the very large hospital bill that we had incurred during treatment and also made follow-up appoint-ments for Conner's three-month scans, as well as nutrition appointments to ensure that his weight gain was adequate. Once his feeding tube was removed, maintaining Conner's weight was more difficult than we realized. Some of the aftereffects of chemotherapy, including acid reflux and his situational depression and post-traumatic stress, affected his appetite adversely.

There had been comfort in our treatment routines and from the reassurances from medical professionals that we were doing the "right thing." Now we were on our own with the unknowns and the "what ifs." It was overwhelming. Cancer can always come back; there are no guarantees. Knowing that, I had to make a conscious decision. Would I live in fear and let it take over my life? Or would I decide take it one day at a time and embrace my life each day and just live it? For the most part, I made a decision not to allow the fear to completely take over. Some days I did better than others. I learned it is important to enlist the support of friends, family, community and, if necessary, professionals to help you keep that promise and to work through your fears. I have also walked alongside friends to support them in looking down that dark, cold abyss of the possibility that their illness will return.

As well, I experienced a renewed sense of self, what is referred to as post-traumatic growth. I would never be the same. Looking back, I wasn't sure I liked the person I was before Conner's cancer. I could often be smug, controlling, and felt the need to be perfect. This new raw and more real person I had become was able to easily feel pain and therefore to recognize pain in others and offer help. I was less quick to judge people and, in time, was less critical of myself. I saw changes in my own children. Life was no longer taken for granted. My boys, who had fought so much as children and were complete opposites, had become friends. Our daughter reached out to us more, calling home just to say hi. And we all appreciated our family time just a little more.

The Journey of Grief

Our western society tells people that they should grieve for one year and move on. My experience with families who have lost a child or loved one is that the second year is often more difficult than the first, because that's when the shock has worn off and the harsh reality of loss sets in. The grieving parent or person is first absorbed in funeral arrangements, then by visitors from near and far. The well-wishers, with their kindness, attention, and sympathy are plentiful the first year and help to blunt the impact of loss. Yet it's that second year, when society and the community often move on, that the grief remains. As my friend Patti once told me, "The silence can be deafening." Going to events where many friends still have children or spouses reminds you of your loss. Birthdays and anniversary dates can be particularly hard.

My friend Diana and her husband, Kiyo, say their son, Josh, speaks to them in symbols. They can often hear him, and they believe that heaven isn't very far away. Their son has been gone nearly two years and, when Dianna speaks of Josh, her voice fills with warmth, longing, and pride as she tells of the great difference he made in the lives of so many, young and old, during his brief eighteen years. The pain is real and palpable for them. Yet the beauty, goodness, and hope Josh inspired with his courage are a living legacy for his parents and for all who knew him.

When my friend Patti lost her son, I would show up on her front porch holding two steaming mochas, while my young children ran about, ready to play with her granddaughter of the same age. I'd smile and wave as I approached her large wooden porch swing where she sat wrapped in a red-and-white patchwork quilt. I'd place the mocha in her hands, kiss her freckled forehead, lower myself gently beside her and we'd just rock together, watching the children play on the front lawn. Sometimes we'd say nothing at all; other times we'd comment on the various nuthatches, robins, and chickadees that landed on Patti's birdfeeder. Some days she'd want to talk about Sam. I'd listen intently, slip an arm around her shoulder, and we would just be.

Losing Becky

Our friend Becky lost her battle to breast cancer. The morning after I had attended a grief meeting at the hospice center, I received the call she had passed. I thought I would be prepared for the news. Instead, I sat on the edge of my bed trying to catch my breath, my feelings overwhelming me as though a giant grizzly bear were pawing and rolling me over, smothering me and making me gasp for air, for life. Her valiant fight was over. Cancer had won, and it was horribly unfair.

Patti came by the following afternoon. I opened my front door to see her standing there, holding a pizza box. The lid was slightly ajar, so I could peer in to see a large, thin-crust, gooey, cheesy pepperoni pizza—my favorite.

"I know how much you like New York–style pizza," Patti smiled stiffly. "I'm sorry about Becky, Honey."

Her face was unreadable. We hugged briefly, and I reached inside the box for a slice of pizza, folding it in half and devouring it hungrily. "This is good," I mumbled between mouthfuls. "Do you want any?" and gestured for her to come inside. She only stayed for a little while. I was surprised that she didn't want to commiserate about death and the grief process. It would take me until years later to understand that her own pain and loss were still too enormous for her to share. Simply being present for me was almost more than she could handle.

"Can we go to the funeral?" my son Patrick asked. He was barely six years old and quite curious, but unsure of what a funeral was. My children had never been to a funeral, had never lost someone close to them. Patrick had known a boy named Daniel from his preschool who died from leukemia, but he was only four at the time, far too young to understand.

"Yes, you can, but they're calling it a celebration," I explained.

"Why?" Patrick looked confused. "Didn't she die? Why would you be happy?"

I thought about his questions. It was confusing to try to draw something happy and joyous from a painful, difficult situation. Forcing my emotions to catapult from deep grief to jubilance was a stretch. So how could I digest and translate that dichotomy into kindergarten terms for Patrick?

"Well, Honey, we're sad Becky is no longer with us. But she's so happy because she's finally in heaven with Jesus. It's a celebration for her and to help us not to be too sad because we have to remember where she is now." I looked into his eyes for some flicker of understanding.

"I guess that makes sense," Patrick answered dubiously and headed off to play with his toys.

After Becky's death, the children kept asking what would happen if I or their father died or if we died at the same time. Patrick asked if Becky would see Daniel, his preschool friend who had died of leukemia, in heaven. Because of their feelings of insecurity, I couldn't be out of my children's sight for more than a few moments. At night, I noticed three sleeping bags slumped across our master bedroom floor, the result of little nocturnal travelers making their way into our room. If I was upstairs, so were they, asking a question or looking for something. If I headed downstairs, likewise. I knew they needed reassurance. We all did.

Initially, I kept trying to convince myself that this was all a very bad dream and that the phone would ring and I'd hear Becky's cheerful voice boom, "Hey, Girl, where ya been?" and all would be as it was. I was in denial. But that phone call from Becky never came, and eventually I would learn to live without her physical presence. Kids returned to school and routines, friends went back to work, and life went on. After Becky's death, I missed my former happy energetic self and it took a long time to heal. Initially, I thought it would be an insult to my friend's honor and memory to act happy and carry on. I was wrong. Becky would've wanted me to live and continue her legacy of kindness and caring.

My husband, Paul, tried to goad me into running to pull me out of my terrible blue-gray fog of grief. He reminded me that it was Becky who would've wanted me to run as he said, "You haven't run in over a week. The half-marathon is coming. Remember how proud she was of your running?" I was so angry with him at the time for prodding me, but deep down I knew he was right. I reluctantly pulled on my running shoes, still complaining all the while.

Much later, I remembered it had been lively Becky who would start that famous backyard water-gun fight with the kids, or give away bags and packages of baby clothes and food to friends and neighbors in need, or host Christmas potlucks and gift exchanges that would make our children laugh and cheer. But Becky was no longer here; she would want me to do these things. Whenever I enjoyed a beautiful moonrise or high moon in the sky, like the one I first saw giant and luminous over Lake Washington from her hospital room, I'd smile knowing that my dear friend was looking down at me. Becky would always be with me.

The day will come when you are no longer a caregiver. Your loved one will be well enough to no longer need caregiving, or death may have taken him or her from you. The kinds of challenges and feelings you will face depend on the outcome. In one situation, you'll have a loved one who will need you to relinquish your caregiver's role so he can begin to resume his new life at whatever level he can. For example, if he is now wheelchair-bound or using a cane to walk, your loved one may still need your assistance, but not in quite the same measure as he did in the hospital. He may require rehabilitation, physical therapy, academic tutoring, counseling, or a combination of all of these. If you have lost a loved one, especially a child, your loss is profound. You will be making funeral arrangements and beginning an intense period of grieving. Often friends and/or family members will step in to help, as this can be traumatic and overwhelming for the bereaved. It is okay to ask for their help. You'll need to redefine your role as you eventually transition back to your "new normal" life after the hospital.

Remember, for most of us, life will never be as it was. The latter situation will take much more time for grieving and be a much different journey than that of a recovering survivor. Regardless of the nature of your outcome, as the crisis ends, so does your caregiving role. Now the healing can begin.

How to Cope After the Hospital

- ♥ If beneficial, continue with support groups you may have joined while your loved one was in the hospital. You may find you still need this support.

- ♥ Reach out to friends and family for help with funeral arrangements and chores during the initial grieving. You may want to select one person to be in charge of these chores for several weeks and months as you recover.

- ♥ When you feel you are ready, volunteer to help with community fund-raisers for your loved one's cause—for example, a cancer fund-raiser or a Ronald McDonald House event. Doing so will help take the focus off of you.

- ♥ Take a class in a hobby that you love or one that you have always wanted to try. Learning new skills and being creative can be a very therapeutic next step.

- ♥ Accept invitations from friends to social events as you feel able to attend. This helps you reestablish yourself in your community and also helps you avoid isolating yourself.

- ♥ Continue to exercise and engage in spiritual activities that bring you solace, comfort, and rejuvenation.

- ♥ Reconnect more deeply with family members such as your spouse, siblings, or children. These relationships often suffer after having such prolonged and intense devotion to one person. When relationships are damaged or become dysfunctional after a stressor like a long-term illness, couples therapy and/or family counseling is recommended.

- ♥ Consider seeking therapy for yourself to help you navigate the post-hospital period, especially if you have debilitating feelings of grief, loneliness, anxiety, or depression that interfere with normal activities and that persist for more than a few months.

RESOURCES

What follows is a limited list of resources to help you function in your daily life as a caregiver, as well as to understand the health issues and treatments facing your loved one who is ill. What I've included is meant primarily to jumpstart your own inquiry into both local and online resources that will boost your ability to be a good caregiver.

A number of the articles I've listed are sourced from professional medical journals. These can sometimes be pretty technical to read and are cited primarily to assure readers that I've done research to support some of the information in my book. I list both the print journal and the online version of the article whenever possible. For the online version, medical publications often assign a DOI (digital object identifier) instead of the more familiar URL (uniform resource locator—or web address).

A wonderful single resource for medical publications that offers free public access to full-text archives of medical literature is the U.S. National Library of Medicine, maintained by the National Institutes of Health (ncbi.nlm.nih.gov/pmc/articles). Also, for more general information, you may want to use jstor.org, a nonprofit site that archives content from more than 2,000 journals. You can read many articles they have online for free or a low fee; digital downloads are fee-based.

Chapter 1: What Can I Do to Help?

CaringBridge.com: You can create a blog on this site for free and share updates and progress reports with your extended network of family, friends, and others. It eases the burden of trying to stay in touch with everyone individually. There are other valuable features on the site as well. Plus you can track the progress of other patients you know.

cleaningforareason.org: When you simply don't have the time and energy to keep your home clean, organizations such as this one can be a lifesaver. It provides free maid service to women undergoing cancer treatment.

DreamDinners.com: Meal preparation is so essential to maintaining the health of your loved one as well as the rest of your family. When you are simply too exhausted to deal with this, this site may be just the answer for you. You can have ready-to-cook nutritious meals delivered to your home, available for pickup, or you can assemble yourself at designated locations (using ingredients already gathered for you).

Chapter 6: Food for the Soul

today.com/health/cancer-menu-project-aims-boost-appetite-after-treatment-2D11624196

This is a great article on the importance of creating appetizing food for cancer patients. Most helpful is their link to the Cancer Nutrition Consortium (cancernutritionconsor tium.org) where you can find nutritional, tasty recipes to keep your patient eating well.

Chapter 9: Taking Care of the Caregiver

Oscar A. Barbarin, Diane Hughes, and Mark Chesler, "Stress, Coping and Marital Functioning Among Parents of Children with Cancer," *Journal of Marriage and Family* (May 1985); 47(2): 473–80. jstor.org/discover/10.2307/352146

This article addresses the stress a cancer diagnosis brings to a family and a marriage. Surprisingly, couples report that drawing upon one another for support and strength during a crisis brings them closer together. This support can diminish if the husband is not present enough as a caregiver for the child or the wife is not available enough for the husband in the home.

Margaret Bevans, RN, PhD, LCDR and Esther M. Sterberg, MD, "Caregiving Burden, Stress, and Health Effects Among Family Caregivers of Adult Cancer Patients," JAMA (Jan 25, 2012); 307(4): 398–403. DOI:10.1001/jama.2012.29.

The article differentiates the informal caregiver, such as a family member or loved one, taking care of a patient at home from a medical professional or hospital staff. The physical and emotional strain on caregivers that is exacted from the constant demands of patient care are relevant and can be extreme, manifesting themselves in weakened immune systems, illness, and chronic fatigue.

Danny Dreyer and Katherine Dreyer. *ChiWalking: Fitness Walking for Lifelong Health and Energy.* New York: Fireside, 2006.

————. *ChiRunning: A Revolutionary Approach to Effortless, Injury-Free Running.* New York: Fireside, 2009.

These books by the Dreyers help you refocus your walking or running routine. They offer simple step-by-step instructions on how to relax while exercising, count your breathing, and focus on your form. It takes the stress out of exercise and brings enjoy-ment (and greater benefit) back into the experience.

Mayo Clinic Staff, "Massage: Get in Touch with Its Many Benefits." mayoclinic.org/ healthy-living/stress-management/in-depth/massage/art-20045743

This article from the Mayo Clinic's online e-newsletter touts the many benefits of mas-sage, which may include reducing anxiety, headaches and digestive disorders, and insomnia brought on by stress.

carepages.com/forums/caregiving/topics/559-alcohol-abuse-1-for-caregivers

An online discussion forum on caregiving. People can post their concerns and obtain support and resources if they feel inclined to drink or overdrink.

Chapter 10: Get Out There!

bentownefoundation.org

This is the website for the Ben Towne Foundation located in Seattle. They're responsible for the cutting-edge cancer research based on immunotherapy. They've currently saved eleven children from terminal leukemia, and there is hope to expand immunotherapy treatment to address other types of cancer such as brain, neuroblastoma, and sarcoma.

go4thegoal.org

This National Pediatric Cancer Program was started by a grassroots movement to provide support to young cancer patients undergoing treatment with care packages around the holidays. My son was the recipient of one of these wonderful gift bags, which contained an iPod, handheld games, candy, and swag. Their fund-raising efforts provide research and hospital building grants to provide quality care for cancer patients and their families.

http://www.makenoise4kids.org/index2.php

A national organization promoting awareness about the underfunding of children's cancer research. Make Some Noise is passionate about increasing research for cutting-edge therapies and family support.

nwsarcoma.org

The Northwest Sarcoma Foundation provides hope, education, and support for cancer patients and their families in the Pacific Northwest. By funding research grants, giving monetary support to families undergoing financial hardship during cancer treatment, and offering education through their outreach programs, the foundation tries to give patients the best possible outcomes and patient care possible.

Susan G. Komen Race for the Cure. apps.komen.org/racceforthecure/?itc=homeaction:1

The official website where you can register or find out more about the Race for the Cure in your area. Learn about who sponsors the foundation and how you can get involved to support breast cancer research and awareness.

Susan G. Komen Breast Cancer Foundation Official Site. answers.com/topic/susan-g-komen-breast-cancer-foundation

Learn more about breast cancer, ask questions, get connected, and find out what is going on nationwide and in your community.

Chapter 11: Pet Therapy

Animal Planet. animalplanet.com/tv-shows/too-cute/games-more/kitten-cam.htm

apl.tv/puppies.htm

This wonderful website shows online videos of puppies, kittens, and other baby mammals. Some webcams are live. Watching the animals in their habitat, you feel as if you are actually there observing. Many report getting fairly attached to the little critters. It's great for people who may not have access to a pet of their own. They're pretty darn cute.

The Humane Society. humanesociety.org

If you're interested in adopting a pet, volunteering to take care of an animal or just want to find out more about what this national organization does in your community, visit their website.

Sue Manning, "Most Pet Owners Believe Their Animals Have a Sixth Sense: Poll," huffingtonpost.com/2011/01/11/pets-sixth-sense_n_807249.html

According to the poll described in this post, two-thirds of pet owners feel their animals have a sixth sense or an intuition about human emotions. Their pets are able to comfort them when they are anxious or ill and/or predict the weather or other impending issue.

Pet Partners. petpartners.org

A volunteer organization that partners animals with people. The volunteers bring a dog or cat to visit a shut-in or very ill patient in need of a furry companion.

Alesia Shute, "Pet Therapy—Why the Furry Friends Help Kids during Illness and Treatment," (May 28, 2010) selfgrowth.com/articles/pet-therapy.

Confirms what many of us have known all along: pets are good for healing and keeping up one's spirits during difficult times.

Therapy Dogs International. tdi-dog.org/OurPrograms.aspx?Page=Hospitals+(Children%27s)

An organization that shares dogs with hospitalized children. If you'd like your child to receive the healing benefits of a canine visit, contact this wonderful organization.

Chapter 12: Therapeutic Options for the Caregiver

M. A. Alderfer, A. Canaan, R. A. Annunziato, and A. E. Kazak, "Patterns of Posttraumatic Stress Symptoms in Parents of Childhood Cancer Survivors," *Journal of*

Family Psychology (Sep 2005); 19(3): 430–40. ncbi.nlm.nih.gov/pubmed/25133839

Discusses and confirms the effects of posttraumatic stress in parents of childhood cancer survivors.

M. A. Alderfer, L. E. Labay, and A. E. Kazak, "Brief Report: Does Posttraumatic Stress Apply to Siblings of Cancer Survivors?" *Journal of Pediatric Psychology* (Jun 2003); 28(4): 281–6. ncbi.nlm.nih.gov/pubmed/12730285

Offers findings that reveal nearly half of all adolescent siblings of young cancer patients reported moderate to severe posttraumatic stress and anxiety. One-fourth of siblings thought their sibling would die during cancer treatment.

L. P. Barakat, M. A. Alderfer, and A. E. Kazak, "Posttraumatic Growth in Adolescent Survivors of Cancer and Their Mothers and Fathers," *Journal of Pediatric Psychology* (May 2006); 31(4): 413–19. ncbi.nlm.nih.gov/pubmed/16093518

Discusses some of the benefits of undergoing the cancer experience as a family. Includes the concept of posttraumatic growth, an experience of positive change from undergoing a highly stressful situation.

A. E. Kazak, S. Simms, M. A. Alderfer, M. T. Rourke, T. Crump, K. McClure, P. Jones, A. Rodriguez, A. Boeving, W. T. Hwang, and A. Reilly, "Feasibility and Preliminary Outcomes from a Pilot Study of a Brief Psychological Intervention for Families of Children Newly Diagnosed with Cancer," *Journal of Pediatric Psychology* (Dec 2005); 30(8): 644–55. ncbi.nlm.nih.gov/pubmed/25133839

Supports the need for providing more early-intervention psychological support in the form of counseling and support groups for newly diagnosed families. These are often grossly underfunded or not included in the current medical model.

Chapter 14: Spirituality as a Source of Strength

Harvard Women's Health Watch, "The Health Benefits of Tai Chi," May 2009. health.harvard.edu/newsletters/Harvard_Womens_Health_Watch/2009/May/The-health-benefits-of-tai-chi

Tai chi is a low-impact exercise that involves slow breathing and movement that helps improve circulation and boosts the immune system.

Health Searches, "Effects of Prayer on Immune System." healthsearches.org/Categories_of_Q&A/Integrative_&_Alternative_Medicine/1335.php

This article gives biological evidence of the benefits of prayer, showing that it reduces the body's production of fight-or-flight hormones (cortisol) in the adrenal gland, thus reducing stress.

Michael W. Smith. *Go West Young Man.* Reunion record label, 1990.

Upbeat contemporary Christian music that I enjoyed with my friend Becky. It delivered a message of hope, faith, and inspiration.

Joni Eareckson Tada. *Pearls of Great Price: 366 Daily Devotional Readings.* Grand Rapids, Michigan: Zondervan, 2006.

A daily devotional reader that provided me with a Bible verse and inspirational message for each calendar day. Written by a quadriplegic who chose hope and a positive attitude over despair.

INDEX